W9-DEM-221

FALL DOWN ANGEL

FALL DOWN ANGEL

by
Rick Steber

Copyright © 2018
Rick Steber
Box 204
Prineville, Oregon 97754

All rights reserved. No part of the material protected by this copyright notice may be reproduced or utilized in any form or by any means, electronic or mechanical, including photocopying, recording or by any informational storage and retrieval system without written permission from the copyright owner.

Cover design by Gary Asher
Page layout by Jody Conners

ISBN: 978-0-945134-71-8

Note

This narrative is based on the adventures of a boy and girl growing up during the era around the Great Depression. These two individuals are absolutely real, but to protect their desire to remain anonymous, some names, events and locations have been slightly altered or changed. This then is the mostly true story of Red Durkee and Jack Small, and how their disparate lives are woven together into a single fabric of circumstance, time, and place.

Books by Rick Steber

Rendezvous
Traces
Union Centennial
Where Rolls the Oregon
Heartwood
Oregon Trail – Last of the Pioneers
Roundup
New York to Nome
Wild Horse Rider
Buckaroo Heart
No End in Sight
Buy the Chief a Cadillac
Legacy
Forty Candles
Secrets of the Bull
Caught in the Crosshairs
A Promise Given
Red White Black
All-Around and the 13th Juror
A Better Man
Three Little Birds
Little White Man
Fall Down Angel
A Cowboy to Love
The Outlaw Tobe Skiens

Tales of the Wild West Series:
*Oregon Trail, Pacific Coast, Indians, Cowboys,
Women of the West, Children's Stories, Loggers,
Mountain Men, Miners, Grandpa's Stories,
Pioneers, Campfire Stories, Tall Tales,
Gunfighters, Grandma's Stories, Western Heroes*

Wild West Trivia
*Cowboy Trivia, Campfire Trivia, National Parks &
Monuments Trivia, Lewis & Clark Trivia, Oregon Trail
Trivia and Oregon Trivia (Volumes One & Two)*

Western Prose & Poems
*Writing the West, Down a Long Dirt Road,
Almost There, Seldom Seen*

www.ricksteber.com

*"There ain't no sin and there ain't no virtue.
There's just stuff people do. It's all part of the
same thing. And some of the things folks do is nice,
and some ain't nice, but that's as far as
any man got a right to say."*

John Steinbeck — *The Grapes of Wrath*

May 1928

Dearest Brother Peter,

 Left outta Montana. Since Ma passed wasn't nothing holdin me back. Run away from reform school. Me an two friends are headed to California. See you when we get there.

      Your Little Sister,

        Red

     ┠┼┼┼┼┼┨

May 1928

Dear Mother,

 Sorry I had to leave home like that. I just couldn't take it any more.
 Trust you understand why I had to go. Hope he didn't take it out on you or the little ones.
 We caught a freight train to Colorado, but we're leaving here as soon as we can. I'm eating okay.
 I'll write again real soon.

      Your son,

        Jack

P.S. Give my love to Nellie and little Donny.

Chapter One

Each of us is born into this world as a perfect little angel. Sometimes—because of hard luck, adverse circumstance, odd quirks of fate and our own reckless decisions—the perfect little angels fall down.

It was a strange twist of fate, and a strange twist of fate only, that brought the odd pair of runaways together at the same place and time. Then, decades later, the weave of their lives overlap once more. This time they discover they share a common past: that once they had hidden in the willows near Ogden, Utah, waiting to catch a ride on the same ill-fated freight train.

On that luckless day, before the train had a chance to gain much momentum, Red Durkee made her move, sprinting to a boxcar and leaping inside the open door. In her short career as a hobo she already knew the front of a train was preferable, that farther back the slack between couplings produced enough jerk to make the ride uncomfortable.

Not far away, Jack Small and his traveling partner, Kelsey Conger, remained hidden in a patch of willows. They were worried a railroad bull might intercept them, and delayed until the last possible second before breaking from cover, racing alongside the train, catching hold of a ladder, climbing up and tumbling into a coal gondola that rocked and swayed to the rising rhythm of speed.

The train crossed the Great Salt Lake on a grade built above the level of the water. For a moment, the track touched solid ground on the tip of the Promontory Mountains, and then it was back to water reflecting a lush palette of pastels. A hot west wind sprang to life, breaking the lake apart and kicking up sparkling mirrors that merrily danced on the tilt of the waves.

After passing the lake, a glaring salt flat stretched white and devoid of life, but reluctantly it gave way to foothills populated with scrubby, gray-green sagebrush. At long last the fire in the sky ducked into the folds of distant hills and the clouds gathered there burned red and yellow, tarnishing quickly. As the evening star emerged, bringing the Milky Way along with it, the freight slowed and pulled onto a siding. The temperature continued to plummet, forcing the runaways to pull on nearly every stitch of clothing they possessed; wearing layers of trousers, shirts and socks.

An eastbound passenger train came through in a rush and the freight train once again returned to the main line and began to roll. The country, now bathed by pale nightlight, gradually underwent a metamorphosis as rolling hills gave way to mountainous terrain with steep grades. From time-to-time, like beads strung on a long necklace, the rocking train blasted into narrow tunnels where the temperature was as warm as the tropics and acrid coal smoke and gritty dust forced the runaways to close their eyes and tuck their noses inside bandanas in order to breathe.

The rails followed the route of least resistance, dropping down the flanks of barren foothills toward the floor of a broad, extensive valley where the Humboldt River twisted and turned lethargically in its wide bed. Three hundred miles away the river disappeared into the thirsty desert at Humboldt Sink. A scheduled stop was made at the sleepy cow town of Elko, Nevada, noted by a cluster of lights in the middle of a murky sagebrush sea. Departing amid a clamor of a ringing bell and barking dogs, the train continued westward, crossing and re-crossing the meandering river on wooden trestles where the sounds of the wheels on the tracks changed, dropping an octave like a horse constantly switching its gait from trot to canter.

For a while a delicate wedge of moon played peek-a-boo behind storm clouds that scurried across the broad expanse of sky. And then, as the train entered the canyon at Palisade, the storm won out. Ominous clouds ruled the dark night and the scene became shockingly violent and chaotic: the din of the lumbering engine, wailing wind, metal groaning, grinding, screeching and cars swaying, jolting, shaking. Brilliant flashes of lightning, followed almost instantaneously by the sharp crack of thunder, exploded like mortar rounds, while frenzied bursts of blue-white light and deafening booms ricocheted back and forth between the narrow confines of the canyon walls. All the while the sinister night grew steadily colder, until the rain froze and came down hard as driven nails.

– Red –

To Red Durkee it seemed the boxcar in which she was riding teetered there on the brink of the summit before plunging down the west side of the mountain toward the broad landscape drained by the Humboldt River. The 14-year-old runaway sensed the rising cadence of speed, and as noise and darkness pressed in around her, her fears became amplified. She brought her knees up to her chest, enfolded arms around her legs and held on tightly, seeking refuge in memories of her childhood.

‡‡‡‡‡‡‡

According to an often told story, when Red was born her mother, Ann Durkee, was astonished at her baby's full head of red hair, so bright it looked like hair set on fire. To the best of Ann's knowledge, nobody in the family had ever had red hair and she had no idea where it came from, could not begin to explain it. Her husband, Marvin, took one look and said, "Hope to hell she don't have a temper to match."

As far back as Red could remember, nobody ever called her Mavis, her given name, she was always just plain Red. Her folks had a little farm in desolate country on the outskirts of Zero, a jerkwater town along the Yellowstone River in eastern Montana. Some of the locals joked that when you start from Zero, all you could do was go up in life.

To support the farm, which was a good place to raise children, Marvin was part owner of the Horseshoe Saloon. It was a place where working men, mostly railroaders, cowhands and sodbusters, could buy a bucket of beer for a nickel, swap stories and play an occasional game of penny-ante poker.

Red was now remembering the details of the saloon: sneaking under the swinging doors and coming up on the side where the floor was scuffed shiny from the leather soles of work boots, and the stale air smelled of beer and smoke. There were a few mismatched tables scattered around the long, narrow room, but mostly they went unused. It was the preferred habit for customers to stand belly-to-the-bar.

The back bar was an elegant showpiece made in England from the finest cherry wood, hand-carved into an ornate floral design, shipped across the ocean and brought up the Missouri River by boat before being hauled overland in a freight wagon. Sometimes cattle buyers, or other men of means, pitched silver dollars and even gold coins over the top of the back bar. Her father liked to joke, saying someday he would move the bar, collect the money and pay off the mortgage on the farm. That was wishful thinking on his part.

An old black man, the only black man within a hundred miles, was the swamper in the bar. He chewed tobacco that dribbled from the corners of his mouth in a perpetual and unsightly drool. Whenever Red was in the bar the swamper took up a position near the door and kept close vigil so he could warn her in case her daddy came ambling up the street.

The drinking men always fancied the times the precocious little redhead, in any one of a dozen colorful dresses, ducked under the swinging doors and came sashaying along the bar. They cheerfully bought her ginger ale and pleaded, "Sing for us."

"You mean my precious little song?"

Selecting one of the men, Red would request, "Please lift me up, mister," and the lucky fellow—slipping big, calloused hands under her tiny pink arms—would in an effortless motion, swing her onto the bar. In a loud, clear voice, to the tune of *The Animal Fair*, she sang:

> *In the shade of the old apple tree,*
> *My dear father is waiting for me.*

He picks up switches,
And takes down my britches,
And I know what's a comin' ta me.

At an early age she learned it advantageous to act out her song, pretending to flip up her dress, and jump as if a switch had actually slapped her backside. Men laughed and guffawed, clapped and pushed coins into her small hands, until the bowl she made with them was overflowing with pennies and sometimes a nickel or even a dime.

"Ya daddy he be a comin' up da street," the swamper called, and she was lifted and quickly set on the floor. She scampered out the back door as her father entered through the front, bellowing, "Where the hell is she?"

He never received a straight answer, and even though he played as though he did not want his wholesome daughter in such a coarse environment, he saw no great harm in it once in a great while. In fact, it secretly pleased him to know how popular she was with his customers.

The men who inhabited the Horseshoe Saloon were not blind to the little girl's ability to tease them in a slightly provocative way. She most certainly had not acquired those talents at home from her mother, who was a very proper and religious woman. The only explanation for her behavior was that she had been born with a burning desire to please men. The future would have to sort out whether this was an innocent blessing from God, or a calamitous curse thrust upon her by a fallen angel.

– *Jack* –

Resting on a mountain of coal in the open gondola, Kelsey Conger idly watched the long, distorted shadows of the train play out over the backdrop of Utah's nothingness. The punch went out of the day as the sun fell toward the distant row of hills. He squirmed deeper in the coal to steal its warmth, closed his eyes and dozed for a few brief moments.

The engineer eased back the throttle and an abrupt shudder cracked through the spine of the freight train. Kelsey came awake with a start. His initial expression reflected fear, not all-out fright, but more the apprehension of a captured sparrow when you hold it in your hands and its tiny heart races wildly. Maybe in that sliver of time between sleep and wakefulness he had a fleeting premonition of the terrible tragedy that was about to befall his best buddy and traveling partner.

Brakes squealed. Black smoke rolled. The train gradually slowed and pulled onto a siding. After they came to a stop, Kelsey remarked, "Gettin' a little chilly, ain't it?"

To Jack, the only significance of the moment was in the realization that his bones were vibrating like a tuning fork freshly rung. Without giving it much consideration he answered, "Yep, sure enough is."

"Sore?"

"Don't know, haven't moved, yet."

One of Jack's eyes was discolored and swollen and his bottom lip was cut. He could feel the pain of the bruise and cut and thought back to his prizefight the previous evening; seeing his opponent's bloody face etched in stark detail. Now he flexed his right hand and became aware of his bruised knuckles. He drew a long breath, exhaled completely, opened both eyes and squinted at a ripe orange ball of sun teetering on the lip of the western horizon. Colors appeared and swiftly drained away.

A crow traipsed across the fading sunset, chased along by a pair of blackbirds. In the distance the steam locomotive idled contentedly. A meadowlark hurried to build one last crystalline melody. Frogs and crickets chimed in with disorganized background noise. Time stretched on a thin, tight wire.

With some difficulty Jack managed to gain his feet in the shifting coal and tried pounding circulation into his stiff muscles. A few stars began to show now as pricks of light in the slate-gray sky. More time passed and then a sudden shrill whistle warned of an approaching train. Out of the west came the advancing locomotive, moving fast. It thundered through the gathering dusk, pushing before it a diffused light that, as it drew nearer, became a powerful beacon. The locomotive shivered the air with concussion as it roared along the steel rails, all power, noise and hissing steam. The tender and three bulky shadows, baggage cars, appeared and disappeared.

In stark contradiction came several passenger cars. Their interiors were gaily lit with electric lights and Jack caught skittering flashes: wood paneling, leather seats, a lamp with a fancy fringed shade, a porter holding a tray of drinks, men playing cards at a table, a woman wrapped in a silver fox coat, and other women giving impressions of print dresses, sheer stockings and flirtatious smiles. A glance here, a nod there, a whiff of imagined perfume, a silently whispered word, all of these fleeting sights and cursory impressions were like dizzying sparks thrown off by the speeding train. As quickly as the train had appeared it departed, leaving behind proof it had been there in the diminishing noise of wheels passing over rails, the caustic smoky residue hanging in the night air, and the red caboose light receding eastward into the night, toward destinations unknown.

After the freight train was again underway, the gay scenes from the passenger cars continued to stay with Jack. He contemplated those many images he had observed and what impressed him most was the disparity. Those travelers rode in the lap of luxury with light and warmth and a myriad of activities to pass their time. He and Kelsey were forced to hunker down in a coal gondola—dirty, cold and hungry—with absolutely nothing but a vague dream to sustain them, a notion that their future might possibly be better out west, somewhere. And then again, he was well aware it might not.

West of Elko, approaching Palisade Canyon, a cold storm overtook them. Kelsey moved up to the next coal car. Ahead of this car, a boxcar's bulky form acted to cut the wind and provide a measure of shelter. As he settled himself, he cupped his hands around his mouth and hollered back, "Move up here. Lot warmer, Jack!"

Jack responded. He tried to get to his feet, but kept sliding in the loose coal. At last he stood and managed to work his way to the front of the car where he stood hunching his shoulders against the raw, buffeting wind. Sleet stung his face and helped wash away his drowsiness. There were bursts of lightning and sharp cracks of thunder. He felt anchored by the nagging stiffness in his arms, from punches he had thrown and those he had absorbed the previous night. He opened and closed his mouth to loosen the jaw that had been jolted by a straight left. The long muscles in his weary legs felt particularly tight. He shivered from the cold, tossed his knapsack forward into the next car, and positioned himself on the edge of the gondola wall. He held onto the hand brake wheel and readied himself to jump. Somewhere up ahead the train whistle sounded a plaintive and distant wail.

As he pushed off, the track dipped, and in direct response the car lurched violently, causing his foot to slip on the wet, greasy metal. Instead of vaulting the short distance to the next car he dropped into the gap between cars, falling and pawing blindly as he fell. Quick reflexes and fast hands came to his defense, allowing him to grab the bottom rung of the ladder, or else he surely would have been swept to his death under the train. His fingers tightly clinched the cold metal, but his body continued downward. Both feet struck a tie, and because of the speed of the train they bounced upward and back.

In less time than it takes an excited heart to complete a solitary beat, a hard-charging wheel and an unyielding iron rail sliced through flesh and bone, severing his left leg between ankle and knee. In that terrifying moment, shock took over and Jack's brain played a series of underexposed black-and-white photographs of his mother, each frame distinct yet slightly altered from the one before. He tried to cry, "Momma," but the word stuck in his throat.

The car shook like a bronc attempting to throw a rider and all Jack could do was grit his teeth and desperately try to hold on. He found an ounce of inner strength and used it to pull himself upward a few inches, and then up some more. Lightning flashed. He became aware that his chest was tight against the ladder bars. His knuckles were white. He was conscious of his breathing, coming hard and fast. He could smell the awful stench of hot grease and absolute terror. He hung there on the ladder, unable to go higher, refusing to let go, while around him sounds were amplified; the clatter of the wheels, the shriek of metal grinding against metal, and the nasty whine of the wind.

Kelsey leaped between cars, leaned down, grabbed hold of Jack's coat and was able to leverage him upward a little at a time. The struggle paid off. Jack was hoisted over the edge and into the safety of the gondola. He laid face down, breathing in the earthiness of the coal and tasting the metallic tang of fear on the tip of his tongue. He turned his head to the side and took a long gulp of the cold night air while sleet collided against his sweat-soaked skin and beads of moisture skated down his fiery cheeks.

He wanted to move, but could not seem to muster the energy it required. He stayed where he was until Kelsey rolled him onto his back. In a voice as taut as stretched barbed wire he asked, "You okay, buddy?"

Although Jack tried to answer he was only able to produce an inaudible grunt. Kelsey removed the bandana from around his neck and wiped sweat and coal dust from Jack's face. More lightning. It was in that moment of transitory illumination when Kelsey saw the empty pant leg. Air rushed from him as if a fist had slammed into his solar plexus. He used it to form a single word, "Jesus."

And then he was working on Jack, cutting through layers of trousers with his pocketknife, tying his bandana around the stub that remained below Jack's left knee, twisting the bandana tightly, using his jackknife to increase his leverage.

Jack must have passed out because when he came awake, Kelsey was leaning over him, speaking directly into his face. He could feel the heat of his breath.

"You've been hurt. Hurt bad." His voice was coarse, throaty, urgent. "Don't try to get up. I'm gonna stop the train."

Kelsey stood, removed his coat, tucked it tenderly around Jack the best he could and reassured him with, "Don't worry. We'll get you to a hospital. You'll be fine."

Kelsey was gone, jumping to the next gondola, jumping again to the boxcar and climbing the ladder to the top. He moved steadily through the wind, with sleet stabbing at him and lightning pulsing around him, running the spine of a boxcar and leapfrogging ahead to the next car. In this manner he maneuvered the length of the train. He reached the tender attached to the locomotive and slid down on the pile of coal to the engine compartment. He hollered at the surprised engineer, "Stop the train! There's been a terrible accident!"

11

Chapter Two

With a rush of smoke and hissing steam the drive wheels spun, screeched and finally grabbed hold, biting against the steel rails. The freight train slowly departed the Elko station, and as the locomotive picked up speed, Red watched the dark figure of a man running beside the open door of the boxcar in which she was riding. He swung through the opening and once inside, went to the far corner and sat with an audible groan.

She was concerned with this man's sudden appearance, but not overly so. She knew that in the morning, when the man saw her, he would think she was just another fellow catching a ride west. She was dressed in several layers of clothes: overalls, loose-fitting flannel shirts, heavy coat and work boots. Her flaming red hair was tucked inside a felt hat. From all outward appearances, she could pass for a young man.

She stayed in her dark corner and watched the man light a hand-rolled cigarette, the match sparking, fire catching, hands cupping the flame and bringing it up to an old and haggard face; thin, with a pinched nose that curved downward on the end like a parrot's beak. Cigarette paper flared and with the shake of a hand, the match was extinguished. As the man inhaled smoke into his lungs, the point of the cigarette shown brightly. Although she felt anxious and unsettled, she tried to reassure herself the old codger really was harmless. Her fingers worked their way into her coat pocket, touching coins adding up to $2.87. A vague feeling of contentment came over her, but it was a fleeting emotion. She had been with friends on the ride to Ogden, but they had moved on to greener pastures and now the disconcerting truth of her situation was obvious: she was an orphan, a runaway from girls' reform school, and totally and irrevocably on her own. Her only hope was Peter, her stepbrother, and she mumbled a silent prayer he would be there for her when she reached California.

The night grew progressively colder and she curled into a ball and slept, only to be awakened by a terrible storm with jagged lightning and booming thunder. With the next flash of lightning she saw the bum standing at the door, pissing into the night, his urine spraying into the cold wind.

Later she heard quick footsteps overhead, someone running across the top of the boxcar, and the noise startled and scared her. Moments later the engineer throttled back, and in succession the couplings bumped against each other as the train began to slow. The bum must have known she was there, perhaps he sensed her sudden fear, because he mumbled into the darkness, "Don't get excited, kid. Ain't no dicks work this section. Sidin' fer an eastbound. That be all."

After waiting the better part of an hour, a freight train approached out of the west, lumbering alongside, and as the probing engine light passed the boxcar, Red shrank back into the shadows. Later she went to the door, looked down the track and saw men with lanterns transfer something from the train she was riding to the eastbound freight. She thought it might be a person on a stretcher, but she was not sure.

Jack Small felt no pain. A thick cloud of morphine hung over the hospital bed and he was content, seeing in his mind a gleaming red tricycle with shiny chrome fenders. He was straddling the tricycle and squeezing the bulb of a horn that made a sound like a raucous goose. *Honk. Honk. Honk.* Someone was standing beside him, a man wearing brown trousers with a sharp crease down the middle of each leg. No body, no face, only those damnable trousers which he concluded must have been worn by his father. His mother told him it was his father who gave him that tricycle.

Another image flickered, this of a professional prizefight. He was in the front row and his father was there with him. In the ring above loomed two enormous black men. One fighter was pinned against the ropes, head down, covering his face with his gloves while his opponent unleashed a paralyzing attack. The crowd noise was dull and muted. The sharp crack of leather against skin was loud and prevailing. In the glare of overhead lights a looping uppercut connected, fractured the jawbone, and in slow-motion the fighter began falling sideways. For a few perilous seconds the ropes held him upright and then his body continued the arc to the canvas. He hit and his body bounced a little as long, pliant muscles in his arms and across his chest went slack. He lay motionless and then slowly, agonizingly so, the head lolled to the side. A gush of blood ran from the fighter's mouth, down his black cheek, and stained the white canvas crimson. Jack looked upward and saw his father's face, eyes wide with excitement, lips pulled into a tense grin across clenched teeth.

And that was it. Those were the only two memories he had of his father: the pair of creased trousers and a face distorted by the excitement of a blood sport. Beyond that, there were a few scant details Jack's mother had shared with him. The family name was originally Schweizerhof. His father's father had lived in Prague and operated a glass-making business. When he died the business was sold and the money divided among his sons. As World War I marched like a shadow across Europe, Jack's father, rather than be drafted into the German army, immigrated to America and anglicized his name to Small.

How his immigrant father, a drinking and gambling man it was said, and Grace, his mother from a privileged Chicago family, ever met and why they married was a total mystery to Jack. But they had, and for a time they lived in the hamlet of Albion, Nebraska, where he and his sister, Nellie, were born. But lady luck had obviously turned her back on the family because his parents divorced when Jack was four years old.

┣┿┿┿┿┿┥

After the divorce, Grace had extravagant plans to move to California and start a new life. The sad reality was that such a move vastly exceeded her means. All she could manage was passage on the train as far as Denver, Colorado, and yet her resolve remained strong. She believed she would make a rosy future for her and her children.

In many ways Grace was an extraordinary woman. She was pretty, poised, willowy, had fine features, flawless skin, lovely brown eyes and auburn hair she occasionally twisted into a bun. But generally she allowed her beautiful hair to cascade freely over her shoulders and down the middle of her back.

Upon reaching Denver, Grace made arrangements to pick up her luggage after she and the children were settled. She purchased a newspaper, and carrying Nellie on her hip and leading Jack by the hand, she walked to a nearby park and found an empty bench facing the street. It was a warm day and she mindlessly dabbed at moisture on her forehead with a handkerchief. When she finished she tucked the kerchief into the valley of her bosom.

She became absorbed in the classified section, first looking for employment possibilities and then a place they could afford to rent. Baby Nellie, wrapped in a light blanket, remained propped against Grace's left hip. Jack was on his mother's opposite side, resting his head against her and watching the goings-on.

Men dressed in suits passed on the sidewalk and many slowed, perhaps hoping to catch the attention of this pretty woman on the park bench. If she happened to look up, they smiled, touched the brims of their hats and spoke some innocuous greeting such as, "Good day, madam."

From the street came a sudden grinding of tires on gravel, followed almost immediately by the sickening crash of metal colliding against metal. A car had run into the back bumper of the car in front. Steam spewed from a cracked radiator and produced a whistle as piercing as a boiling teapot. Curious spectators gathered, and from this crowd emerged a man with a flushed complexion. He walked directly toward Grace and the children, removed his hat with a practiced flourish and spoke to Grace. "I beg your pardon, ma'am, but since you caused me to run into that car I thought I should at least meet you. My name is Frank Steinman."

"I caused...how could I?"

Frank held up a hand, and paying absolutely no attention to the baby in her arms or boy flanking her said, "I glanced in your direction and forgot about looking at the road."

Frank took notice of the lady's left hand. Her ring finger bore no wedding band, but a white mark was there to indicate one had recently been removed. He smiled and charged ahead like a horse spying an open gate. "You're a very lovely woman, very lovely indeed. I realize it may seem rather presumptuous of me, but yet in light of the unusual circumstances I feel compelled to ask, would you consider having dinner with me this evening?"

Grace tapped the newspaper on her lap with a forefinger. "The children and I just arrived. I'm looking for a place we could rent."

"You shall be my guests, all three of you," he said, making an encompassing gesture with a roll of one hand. "I know a hotel where you will be most comfortable, and come tomorrow I'll help you find a nice bungalow at the edge of town so the little ones will have room to roam."

With his gracious words, and especially his acknowledgement of the children, the climate of her heart warmed considerably. She quickly abdicated and accepted the offer. Two weeks later Grace took Frank Steinman as her second husband.

<hr />

The morphine was now playing tricks on Jack's thinking. He abruptly switched from thoughts of his mother to remembering the dazzle of lightning and repercussions of thunder bouncing off the rocky walls of Palisade Canyon. He was absently rubbing his hands together, trying to feel them, feel something: pain, panic, fear, anything. This precise image was suddenly replaced with a series of disjointed impressions and visions. Ideas that, like random tumbleweeds before a strong wind and without something as tangible as a barbed wire fence to come up against, just kept rolling and drifting in a morphine haze; drifting...no meaning, no purpose for being, no significance...just drifting.

He became vaguely aware of the sensation of cold rain splattering against his face. He wondered if God was crying for him. Then Chet, his mother's third husband, was commanding him, "Jack, would you please say the blessing." But with Chet it was never a question, always a command. A perplexing thought crossed Jack's mind, that God must be kept awful busy cataloging prayers three times a day, listening to people all over the world thank him for the bounty they were about to receive. Surely He must know how appreciative mankind was without everyone having to say so. After Jack ran away from home—more precisely he ran away from Chet—he never thanked God for his food, not even a single time. Still, at that moment, he was imagining lying on a bed of wet coal in a gondola and he felt closer to God than ever before. Was it God who kept him from falling. Falling? He was falling in his dream and taking urgent breaths. His mother stood at the kitchen screen door drying her hands on her apron. She turned and allowed the door to bump against her backside as the spring pulled it shut. He was reaching to touch his shirt, the place where he kept pinned the picture of his mother, and when he felt it there a glimmer of hope surged inside him, reassured him, and made him feel safe and protected. A blazing light was being shined into his eyes. He blinked and saw Kelsey.

"We're transferring you to another train and taking you to the hospital in Elko. Hang on. You're doin' just fine."

▭▭▭▭▭▭▭

Jack opened his eyes, pupils dark and dilated. Kelsey really was there. Jack tried, but failed to bring his friend into focus, managed to whisper, "My leg?"

"Yeah, buddy, it's your leg."

After that brief exchange, Jack slipped back into unconsciousness. Time passed—seconds, minutes, hours—and as imperceptibly slow as a December sun struggling to burn away a cold river fog, he again began to become aware. This time his throat felt constricted and irritatingly dry. He flicked his tongue to tentatively touch his parched lips, groaned involun-

19

tarily, and was unsure where the sound was emanating from. He sank below the surface of understanding. Eyelids fluttered. Crickets stirred and began a strident song in the bush outside the window. He imagined grasshoppers—brilliant flashes of white, yellow, red and black—leaping into the air, hanging, rattling, dropping to the safety of tall, dry grass. He breathed in the rich aroma of sagebrush and the bitterness of willow bark drifting up from the thickets bordering the Humboldt River. From somewhere a raven cawed.

He now saw his stepfather, and Chet had his belt off and was moving forward. His face was emotionless, and beyond him Jack saw the faces of his mother and sister and baby brother, Nellie and Donny. There was Sister Elizabeth from "Our Lady of the Forgiving Heart Welfare and Orphanage Home" looking very disapprovingly. He was now standing directly in the path of a driverless automobile racing down a steep hill. No, he was in a lake. He was drowning. He was on a beach and crows were pecking at his eyes. Pain drove a spike between his temples and yanked him awake. It was such a terrific jolt that he was powerless to move, could only lie there and accept the pounding in his head, pounding so intense it shook the pillow. He began to sweat feverishly and felt sick to his stomach.

The next time Jack woke up, the headache was mostly gone. He opened his eyes and squinted at the harsh light. He saw through the window that leaves were trembling in a breeze and concentrated on those leaves, concluding each leaf had a shiny side that reflected sunlight and a dull side that did not. It was in that brief moment of lucidness that he became acutely aware he was alive. He felt freshly laundered sheets softly touching his skin, smelled medication and cleaning solutions, and heard the melodious cadence of people talking outside in the hallway. But interspersed within the framework of such verifiable evidence, came illogical flashes of rail cars and bright lights.

Jack blinked hard several times and struggled to keep his eyes open. When he did, he found his head had been elevated onto a pillow. He was looking downward to where there was a singular rise in the blanket on his bed and reasoned this had to be his right leg and foot. Extending off the bed on the left side, all the way to the far edge, was a nearly flat plane.

"My leg!"

He comprehended his left foot and part of his leg were missing. He was maimed, disfigured, mutilated, a goddamn cripple. With effort, he pulled the pillow from under his head, placed it over his face and held it tightly, trying to suffocate himself. But he could not hold it tight enough, and like a series of rogue waves washing over him, he felt anger, shame, sorrow and pity. He began to cry. There had been a time when he was very young and had fallen on a sidewalk and scraped skin off one knee. His mother had scooped him into her arms and held him while he cried. When there were no more tears he lay with his head in the warm hollow between her breasts, listening to the strong, steady beat of her heart. In that moment he found absolute contentment. That sense of contentment was what he now needed most, but it eluded him.

"How you doing? Jack, can you hear me?" Kelsey was talking to him.

Jack removed the pillow. His eyes were red and swollen. He used the heels of his hands to wipe at the remnants of moisture on his cheeks. His skin color was good, ruddy and healthy. One of the nurses must have attempted, without much success, to comb his hair. Kelsey commented, "You sure enough could use a haircut."

"I...I...I lost my foot."

"I know. But it ain't the end of the world. They saved most of the leg. I talked to the doc and he said they can give you a fake leg and most people won't even know, won't be able to tell. You'll hardly limp or nothin'."

The room was quiet and then Jack broke the silence. "How did you stop the train?"

"Ran the spine." Kelsey grinned. "Glad I didn't think about it 'fore I did it. It was so damn dark, raining and sleeting, lightning, smoke getting in my eyes, slippery as hell...don't know how I kept from falling."

Jack breathed in a harsh whisper, "You saved my life."

"Just wish I'd never called you up there. Want me to get in touch with your folks?"

"Hell, no. Ain't nothin' anyone can do for me, 'cept leave me the hell alone." Jack slammed his eyelids shut.

"Get some rest. I'll swing by a little later." Kelsey patted Jack's shoulder before quietly slipping from the room.

Chapter Three

Marvin Durkee was an adequate provider, a good father and a genuinely honorable man. He stood a solid six-feet-two inches in his stocking feet and weighed nearly two hundred muscular pounds. He was the only man in the town of Zero, besides the preacher, who did not feel the need to pack a gun.

When it came to Red, Marvin was a pussycat. Most mornings his little girl traipsed into the kitchen in her pajamas, barefooted and sleepy-eyed, and crawled onto her daddy's ample lap. He wrapped his big arms around her and held her while taking sips every now and then from a steaming mug of coffee.

Stepbrother, Peter, was 11 years older than Red and from her mother's first marriage. He worked after school restocking shelves for Mr. Logan in his mercantile store. Because Peter was busy, it fell to Red to help her father with the evening chores. She enjoyed hand feeding hay to Betsy the milk cow, the team of horses, Dandy and Mike, and the saddle horses, Sketter and June. She gathered eggs from the hen house and tagged along while her father slopped the hogs. They had fun working together.

Performing chores with her father gave Red a sense that life was a happy routine, stable and enduring. She took the most pleasure when they were in the warm confines of the barn and she could breathe in the aroma of last summer's hay, the sour sweat of the animals and the earthy fragrance of fresh manure. But all those wonderful times came to an abrupt end with the dreadful flu epidemic of 1918 that rolled over the land and touched nearly every family in America. Healthy folks woke up in the morning feeling fine, suffered stomach cramps by midmorning, and those who were the most susceptible were often dead by nightfall.

Marvin took sick with the virus, and although he fought valiantly, his sturdy frame was soon reduced to little more than flesh and bone. One morning he whispered to his wife to fetch the attorney, that he needed to talk to him. When Ralph Thurman arrived, Marvin weakly instructed him, "Draw up my will. Make sure everything goes to my wife and kids."

Mr. Thurman dutifully wrote a basic will in legal form, put the pen in Marvin's right hand and arranged the paper so he could sign his name. It was a struggle for him to hold the pen, let alone sign his name, but he forced himself to complete the task. The attorney folded the papers and promised, "I'll file this at the courthouse." But he had other ideas in mind.

Along with her husband, Ann Durkee also came down with the flu. Peter assumed the duties of head of the household and made arrangements to have Red live in town at Mrs. Braxton's boarding house. Peter hired a nurse to come in, but after only four days, Ann felt she was beginning to recover and sent the nurse away.

The following day, Sunday morning, Ann placed a call to her daughter at Mrs. Braxton's boarding house. She was calling to say that the crisis at home was easing. Marvin's fever had finally broken and within a few days he'd be as good as new.

But as she was speaking to Red, telling her these things, she suddenly dropped the mouthpiece. It bumped into the wall three or four times before swinging free.

"What is it, Momma?"

Marvin had given a sharp yelp, followed by a long, weary sigh. Ann rushed to the room, gathered her husband in her arms, and felt his tired and congested heart surrender to a directionless beat. His damaged lungs struggled to gulp one last breath, and like a hard-charging river consumes a bank of sand—sand crumbling, falling, washing away and leaving nothing—he exhaled and life ebbed from his body.

⊞⊞⊞⊞⊞⊞

Now the train Red was riding eased down the face of the Sierra Nevada Mountains and she knew, if her father had lived, her life would be so very different than it was at this moment. The best she could hope for now was Peter would be there to welcome her when she reached San Francisco.

Her trip west from Ogden, for the most part, had been uneventful, except for one incident; the bad storm west of Elko and the trepidation she felt when someone ran over the top of her boxcar. After that the train stopped, and an eastbound freight had pulled alongside and stopped. She had been fearful she would be discovered and tossed off the train in the wilderness.

Even now, the sullen bum who hopped aboard the boxcar on the outskirts of Elko remained across from her in the far corner. Every once in a while he got up to stretch his legs or relieve himself. Red did not expect every traveling companion to have the personality of Railroad Bill, the first professional tramp she ever met. He was one of a kind and she was grateful for having made his acquaintance, and for having had him teach her the ropes.

25

By the time the train crossed over the Rocky Mountains and reached the floor of the Imperial Valley, the air had warmed considerably. As they neared Sacramento, the bum dropped off without so much as a "goodbye" or a "see-ya-all-later." With his departure Red took her turn at the doorway and then sat, legs dangling outside, enjoying the weather and the scenery. The country, mile upon mile, was fertile and lush with fields of rice, grain and row crops.

The train topped the highest point on the Sonoma foothills and began the final gentle descent to the Pacific shores, snaking around hills that afforded a remarkable view of the blue waters of San Francisco Bay. Wind whispered across the tops of the hills making the tall brown grasses shimmer in erratic waves, and bringing with it unfamiliar smells of salt water and sea life. It seemed as though all the many promises California had to offer were unfolding before her very eyes, and with zealous anticipation Red looked toward a bright future.

⊦⊦⊦⊦⊦⊦⊦

Jack, from his hospital bed in the cowboy town of Elko, looked out the window at the sullen ridges cut by brooding draws as gray and well-defined as scars. If he could somehow be whole again he would run the backbone of those ridges with carefree joy, until strength and stamina failed him. But he knew he would never again be able to run like that. In frustration he ground his teeth until his jaw ached. Time dissolved into inconsistent intervals between failure and shame, depression and despair, hopelessness and despondency.

Kelsey swept into the room, the perfect picture of cheerfulness, exclaiming as he came, "How you doing today, buddy?"

Jack caught the telltale scent of sage and the pungent aroma of wood smoke. He asked, "You camping?"

"Did last night."

"Thought the railroad was putting you up at the hotel. They didn't up and give you the boot, did they?"

"They paid for my room the first couple nights. Hey, I never expected them to play mother hen. After all, to them we're nothing but a couple of damn hobos."

"You're not eating decent then, are you?"

"You won't believe what happened yesterday," Kelsey said, smiling broadly. "I left here, walked through an alleyway, smelled the sweet smell of baking and watched a woman set a pair of pies in the window to cool. I just happened to liberate one—golden-brown crust, blueberry, sweet as honey—and ended up eating the whole damn thing. Middle of the night I paid the price. My stomach turned inside out. Sick as a dog I was.

"Then this morning I find a tarp in the middle of the road." He switched to a whisper and leaned toward Jack. "Actually I stole it off a woodpile and sold it to a fellow passing through town. He gave four bits." He stood straight and his voice returned to normal. "Had me a big breakfast—sausage, eggs and pancakes with strawberry jam. So you don't have to worry none 'bout me. I be livin' high on the hog."

Jack reached for a pair of crutches leaning against the wall by the bed. "Watch this." He slid his good leg, followed by the stump, off the bed. Standing, tucking the crutches under his arms and using them for balance, he made a circle around the room and returned to sit on the edge of the bed.

"Terrific. Didn't figure you'd be down long. You'll be out of here 'fore you know it."

"Doctor said they have to wait until the swelling goes down. Then they fit me with a fake leg." Jack waited a little and added, "I really don't expect you to hang around here, Kelsey."

"I was gonna—"

Jack held up a hand. "Hear me out. You could do just like we planned, get to California and catch on with the movies. I'll join you when I can. Probably not a big market for a one-legged fighter or stunt man, but I'll find something."

Kelsey dropped his chin. His voice was distant. "I called Mom last night. Don't worry. I never mentioned your accident. Anyway, she wants me to come home. I was thinking, if you don't need me, I'd sneak in a quick visit. When I get back you'll sure enough be ready to hit the road. She promised to wire money for a ticket. Imagine, riding the rails as a paying customer."

"Nothing you can do here." Jack shrugged. "Go."

After Kelsey left the room, Jack knew all too well they had parted company and from that day forward their lives would be like two trains speeding in opposite directions. The way he had it figured, Kelsey would follow in his old man's footsteps, sell merchandise on the road, marry a local gal back home, and they would have a passel of screaming kids. "Yep," he thought to himself. "That'd be the size of it. For Kelsey, the adventure is pretty much dead and done with."

He felt a feathery tickle localized on the thin flap of skin between big toe and the toe next to it. An itch so acute, so clearly defined and intense, that he started to reach under the covers to scratch it, and then remembered he no longer had a left foot. The severed appendage was playing a cruel trick on him. He hated the unjust irony of it, inhaled sharply and laid his head back against the downy pillow, feeling a jagged pang of frustration and self-loathing.

The following morning, a nurse waltzed into the room saying, "What a wonderful day it is." Her smile was genuine, but unfortunately not contagious. She moved around the bed and Jack noticed the starch in her white cotton uniform made a scraping sound as she gracefully threw open the blind with a cheery, "Let's get a little light in here."

He squinted as golden sunlight flooded the room.

"Why did you have to go and do that?"

The nurse moved so close he could smell rubbing alcohol, soap, and a vague trace of last evening's perfume. Ignoring his comment she announced, "Let's take your temperature." She deftly flicked a thermometer and slid one end between his unwilling lips and under his tongue. Next she took his wrist, and with cool fingers probing for his pulse, she quickly concluded it was strong and rhythmic and released her grip. She wandered away from her patient.

"Look, there's a squirrel. See the way he jumps from limb to limb? How do they do that? It's like they can fly; so nimble, so quick and strong."

In Jack's mind, it seemed as though the nurse was mocking him. The squirrel was everything he was not. He pouted. The nurse returned to check the thermometer. "Perfectly normal." She shook the mercury into the bulb with another flick of her wrist.

"You're doing so well."

Her well-practiced delivery and earnest tone were meant to encourage and motivate Jack. She turned slightly away, back toward the window. "If you keep improving, maybe in a few days you can go home."

She took several steps toward the doorway. Jack wanted to yell, "I don't have a home!" Instead he made a vague accusation. "Someone stole my photograph, the one I had pinned inside my shirt."

She hesitated and then turned to face him. "I don't believe anyone purposely took anything. Your clothes were cut off you. We had to determine how badly you were injured. Anyway, what could be saved was washed and you will find those clothes, along with your knapsack, in the closet. If something happened to your property, if a photograph was lost, I'm truly sorry."

▭▭▭▭▭▭

Jack received a letter, handwritten in pencil on lined paper.

Dear Jack,

Made it home. Having a paid ticket and breakfast, dinner and supper served in a dining car is a great way to travel. I slept in a bed. Not at all like hoboing.

The folks were waiting for me when the train pulled in. Mother was crying. The old man actually put his arms around me and gave me a hug. About puked.

Your momma come to the house yesterday. I did like you said. Told her you went on to California. Told her you'd most likely drop her a line when you got settled.

Things are going pretty good here. My old man give up selling on the road and done bought out McMurray's Hardware. He's running the store. He's home every night and don't know if that's good or bad, but he plays catch with me of the evenings and says he'll think about buying me a used Ford. Mind you nothing very fancy. So, guess I'll keep my nose to the grindstone for a little while and see what happens.

Write me when you got a chance. Let me know how you're making out. If it gets too bad you can always come home. See you around the bend.

Your friend,

Kelsey

Jack thought he was prepared for the eventuality that Kelsey was not coming back, but he was not. He felt blindsided with loneliness. He was without friends, or family, and without his left leg too. His dreams were gone and so were most of his ambitions. He was emotional and sensitive. Almost anything—a memory from the past, a smell from outdoors, a sound from a passing train, a wayward thought—could cause tears to well up and burn his cheeks.

He cried for himself. He cried for his mother and sister and brother. When he had cried away those sorrows he fell asleep and dreamed of a black turkey vulture sweeping across the circular sky, sailing low. Then with effortless brush strokes of its wings, the big bird landed on the railroad track, hopping from tie-to-tie, turning its hideous head this way and that. Sunlight sparkled off vermilion wattles. The disgusting bird gave a heartless caw that was both caustic and merry. The plaintive wail of a coyote answered, and soon the sleek animal came trotting into view. The buzzard responded by spreading its wings and hunching over, giving a vulgar, raspy hiss, snapping its beak and flashing yellow eyes full of hateful venom. The coyote refused to be intimidated. It ventured nearer and growled. The bird rejected all pretense of dominance, took two or three short hops, and launched itself into awkward flight.

What the ugly bird left behind there in the middle of the railroad tracks was a boot firmly laced. Protruding from the top was a stubby, blood-covered chunk of leg. Straightaway the coyote claimed his prize and began making crepitate noises as it gnawed on flesh and bone.

Jack awoke from his ghastly dream in a cold sweat, gulping air, still hearing the godawful chewing noises ringing in his ears. He sat, spun his leg over the edge of the bed, and after a moment of hesitation he stood, wavering uncertainly on his one good leg. With the greatest of effort he managed to hop to the window. There he caught his balance by grabbing the casing. Beyond the thin pane of glass the atmosphere was cool and clear, the hills hard-edged and one-dimensional. Stars twinkled on and off in the truculent night. He could not look away.

"God help me!"

The window glass fogged with a light mist from his breath, distorting his view. Muscles in his arms began to shake. A church bell rang three times. A puff of wind rattled the glass.

With single-minded concentration, Jack reminded himself he was still, at heart, a fighter. Had he not been told he had a shot at winning a world championship belt? Sure, losing a leg was a hard blow for anyone to absorb, but never count a fighter out. He knew he might be down, but by god he'd beat the count. His lips curled over his teeth in a fierce grimace. Nostrils flared. He vowed to find the personal courage required to not only survive, but to fight on.

Out there in the darkness somewhere west of Elko, the coyote and the buzzard continued to haggle over leftovers.

Chapter Four

Red stood on a street corner in Oakland watching people and automobiles moving along the sidewalks and streets. She had Peter's address, and after stopping at a filling station to ask directions, began walking in the direction she was given. As she moved from the city to the outskirts, and finally into the country, the road deteriorated to not much more than wayward ruts, interspersed with chuckholes glistening with muddy water from a storm that had recently passed that way. But the sun came out again and her spirits were high as she walked and whistled *Sweet Georgia Brown*.

She wondered about the many years it had been since she last saw Peter. Now he was married and operated his very own chicken ranch. He had done well for himself, she was sure of that, and visualized him as a slightly older version of the young man who blew her a kiss from the train station the day he departed Montana.

She located the mailbox with his name on it and followed a tapered lane ending at the front porch of a small white house with faded blue shutters and a sagging front porch. The late afternoon sun reflected off San Francisco Bay and sent ivory streaks of sunlight through the leaves on the trees draped low over the house.

She was full of animated energy and took the stairs leading to the front porch two at a time. Her heavy boots clomped against the boards. She rapped her knuckles solidly against the screen door. The door slapped loosely against the frame. Behind the house, in one of the long barns, came the clucking of a proud hen announcing her new egg. Out on the road an automobile rattled and splashed through puddles, heading toward the city.

┉┉┉┉┉

Peter opened the door, but remained mostly hidden behind the screen. He cautiously eyed the disheveled traveler standing on his front porch; saw the soiled clothes and face sunburned, wind chafed, and sooty. The only clue to the identity of this stranger, if Peter had picked up on it, would have been the tangle of red hair oozing from beneath a drab and shapeless hat.

"Yeah, whataya need?"

┉┉┉┉┉

Red did not immediately recognize the man standing in front of her. His hair was thinning and combed straight back in an unfamiliar style. His face was too thin, too angular. He was gangly and dressed in a pair of coveralls and a short-sleeve cotton shirt. He could have passed for a North Dakota plowboy. But something—perhaps it was the set of his jaw or the way one eye was slightly cocked—registered with her. She dropped her dilapidated canvas tote at her feet while a grin tugged at the corners of her mouth.

"What, you don't recognize your own flesh and blood?"

Peter stepped around the screen door for a better look.

"Well, guess you found me."

"Guess I did. I'm here. I made it. Just like I said I would."

He held open the screen door. "Well, come on in."

Red picked up her bag and slipped past him as he mumbled, "Was about to fix a bite to eat. You're probably hungry. Best wash up. Bathroom's down the hall, first door on the left."

"Where's Brenda?"

┣┿┿┿┿┿┫

Peter stopped abruptly. What he did not say or could not say, was more important than what he actually chose to say. He did not say that he and Brenda had exchanged sharp words, words that were driven into his heart like a lance. He did not say she stormed from the house with a bulging suitcase in hand and the dresser drawers left flung open. He did not say that in the aftermath of her leaving, the stuffy, stale air trapped inside the house had made it seem like a prison to him, and that at night he felt the sharp stab of loneliness the most. It was in those hours he wished he could die. Wished he *would* die.

"Guess I might as well tell you. Brenda and me, we ain't together no more. She never liked the work, the chickens. She went away."

"I'm sorry."

His eyes began to water and he turned away. Red could think of nothing more to add and shuffled off to the bathroom where she scrubbed her face, neck, hands and forearms with Ivory soap. Even though she washed vigorously, when she went to dry she left brown smudges on the white towel. She washed again.

She entered the kitchen with freshly scrubbed, ruddy pink skin. She had attempted to run a brush through her hair, and settled for tying the unruly mop into a ponytail, using a short piece of leather lace.

35

Peter had tenderized a pair of thin round steaks with the back of a butcher knife and they sputtered on a sheen of bacon grease in an iron skillet. Potatoes sizzled in a frying pan. Red asked if there was anything she could do to help. He directed her to the cupboard for plates and glasses, and then to the utensil drawer. During dinner she ate ravenously and chattered between and around bites, telling things that happened at reform school and about Bertie and Zelda, Railroad Bill, the carnival, and other snippets from her trip west.

He dabbled at his food and gazed out the window, to where the hills had taken on a quality as solid as stone. He allowed her words to casually wash over him until she asked, "Since you're short-handed, I was wondering if you could use a little help around here? I don't expect to freeload. I work like a man."

"Well, you're not a man, you're a girl and it's about time you started looking and acting like one."

Peter's words, and the vehemence with which he spoke them, caught Red off-guard and she recoiled by pushing her empty plate from in front of her. "What do you mean?"

"I've been sitting here trying to figure out what the hell I'm gonna do with you."

"Your letter...."

"Maybe you read more between the lines than was actually there."

"I thought you invited me...."

"There ain't much profit in chickens. I can't afford to hire you or nobody. In this business the big boys are squeezin' out the little guy like me. They buy in volume. Sell in volume. I can't compete. Hell, I'm barely scrapin' by as is."

"That's okay. I understand."

But she did not understand, and she did not know what she was going to do. She supposed she would have to find a job somewhere.

He took a deep breath and exhaled. "I hate to do this, but I'm gonna make a call on your behalf."

He went to the other room and talked on the telephone. Red heard only snippets of the conversation: "...she dropped in on me...riding freight trains...ain't got no...she needs...no, now listen to me...she's my sister, half-sister...she's just a kid and green as grass...maybe you could put in a good word...thought Marge could help her out, at least until she gets on her feet...."

He hollered, "How old are you?"

"Be 15 in a few months."

He returned to his telephone conversation. When he came back in the kitchen the table was cleared and the dishes were in the sink. Red poured a cup of coffee and brought it to him. He picked up the cup, paused to puff ripples across the surface, took a tentative sip and set the cup on the table.

The telephone rang. He went to answer it. When he returned he said, "I spoke with Brenda and she's got you lined up. She has a friend, Marge Davenport, a businesswoman with a heart of gold—knows all the high society folks in San Francisco—and she's gonna put you up for a while, until you can get on your feet. I'll take you to her place in the morning. You're gonna like her. She's a fine lady. She'll teach you what you need to know and find you a job, too."

<hr>

The following morning Red rose early and tagged along with Peter as he went about his chores. She wore a pair of his black rubber boots, her feet slopping around in them as she progressed up and down the long rows of nests. She reached under setting hens to steal eggs, moving slowly to avoid being pecked, and gingerly placed the warm eggs in a cold metal bucket. She was reminded of all the times she and her father had done chores and it pleased her to know she was helping Peter.

Afterward, as they were walking to the house, she noticed a hawk hanging by its feet in a high branch of a dead tree. She made a comment about the bird, and Peter explained, "I killed it, hung it there to ward off other hawks."

"Does it work? Does it keep them away?"

"Wishful thinking. Face it, ain't no live hawk in the world gonna pass up a chance at a pullet."

They reached the back steps and she pulled off the rubber boots. He said, "Sure went a lot faster with you helpin' out. Thanks."

"I can stay if you want."

"That wouldn't work. You best get your things together. I'll run you to town after we've had something to eat."

<hr/>

Peter drove his Ford Model-A pickup—once shiny black, but now spotted with gray filler until it looked like a pinto horse, tires so worn the rubber seemed attached to the wheels by a feeble prayer—into San Francisco. Upon reaching the Tenderloin—a neighborhood located in the flatlands on the southern slope of Nob Hill—he slowed the pickup and turned into the short driveway of a house that gave the appearance of an impenetrable fortress. The three-story house, made from quarried rock, stood on a slight hill surrounded by an imposing wall made from the same rock. He stopped at a substantial wrought iron gate and tooted the horn. A man dressed in a dignified blue uniform appeared and opened a small side gate.

"This is it," Peter said.

Red was in awe of the building. "Looks like a castle."

He leaned across the seat, pulled the handle on the passenger door and pushed it open. "Once you get settled, give a call and let me know how you're doing. Good luck, kid. Wish I could have done more."

His abruptness flustered Red, and all she managed was to give him a quick peck on his right cheek and thank him. She swung her legs outside and stepped from the truck. She had the presence of mind to grab her tote from the bed of the pickup, but she seemed uncertain what to do next.

"Go on. You'll be fine."

He put the pickup in reverse and departed in a puff of sour smoke. The man in uniform opened the small pedestrian gate a little wider. As Red drew near he said, "Welcome, Miss Durkee. Mrs. Davenport is expecting you."

He led the way inside to a two-level room. On the slightly elevated upper level was an elaborate fountain featuring nude marble maidens emerging from a pool of dancing water. Persian rugs and an array of beautifully upholstered lounges, love seats and settees were grouped like intimate friends around the spacious room. From the ceiling hung an ornate chandelier of gleaming gold and beveled glass that radiated a lively prism of colors. Candles flickered. Incense permeated the air with a thin cloud of exotic smells.

She stood there unmoving, trying to grasp such opulent grandeur, until the man prompted her, saying, "This way, please." He led the way up a wide staircase covered with a long runner of blue carpet that, like a silent cascading waterfall, spilled from one stair to the next. Her hand reached and touched the smooth surface of a banister carved from olive gray, Siam teak. It hugged the stairs in an artistic spiral of highly polished wood.

On the second floor landing a colored woman of substantial girth was carrying an armload of linen. Red greeted her with, "Howdy," but the woman never made eye contact, nor gave any indication she heard the greeting. Upon reaching the third floor, the man stopped in front of a massive door. He used the golden lion head tapper to make his presence known and announced, "Your guest has arrived, Mrs. Davenport."

"Very well." The voice from inside was deep-throated and sultry. After a moment the door opened, revealing a plump woman of indeterminate age, attired in an exquisite dress the color of pink topaz—probably silk thought Red—and made even more wondrous with tasteful frills and fancy lace. Silver hair was piled on top of the woman's head in a tight bun and she had slashes of black for eyebrows, blue-green eyelids, chubby red cheeks, and lips painted a color that came close to matching the shade of the dress.

"Marge Davenport," the woman said extending her hand. "And you must be my little hobo."

Red noticed shiny diamond rings and felt the way the hand seemed to engulf her hand. It was almost as if she was being absorbed into the enormous presence of this grand lady. She wanted to say something, an acknowledgement of some sort, but could not find the proper words.

"Step inside, honey," directed Marge. She moved away, crossing the room to retrieve her gold cigarette case from a freestanding ashtray. She took a seat on a white leather chesterfield in front of a bay window that revealed a marvelous view of the city. She motioned for Red to join her. Marge looked her over with an appraising glance and announced, "I do believe I can do something with you. First we need to get you cleaned up, and then into some presentable clothes. After all, fine feathers make a fine bird."

━━━━━━━

Marge was secure in the knowledge she could do as she wished because, to her, finances were of little concern. If she occasionally took an unfortunate girl off the street, or in this case a wandering hobo, and provided her the necessities of a good life, then she felt as though she was giving back to society. She reached and touched a buzzer on the end table beside her.

A provocatively feminine voice came through the speaker, "Yes, Mrs. Davenport?"

"Which one of the girls is having her *flowers*?"

"Helen is."

"Send her up, please. Tell her I want her to run uptown and do some shopping for me. And please tell Martin to have my car ready."

"Yes, Ma'am."

A moment passed and then Red questioned, *"Flowers?"*

"That's what we call it," Marge said taking a puff of her cigarette and exhaling smoke, "a woman's time of the month, her menstrual period."

"Oh," Red said, and although a little embarrassed, she added, "Momma called it *the curse*. The girls at school called it *the sickness*."

"Yes, and isn't *flowers* a much nicer word?"

There was a polite rap on the door and Marge called, "Come in, please."

Helen arrived in the room with a rush. She was tall and stylish, with precise features, dusky-blue eyes, and long auburn hair. Her slender waist was emphasized with a white belt cinched around a turquoise dress that twirled like a summer breeze had followed her into the room. She tossed a wink and a cordial smile in Red's direction.

"Helen, this is Miss Durkee. We need to pretty her up a smidgeon."

"Of course," Helen responded.

Marge went to a dresser, pulled out a small drawer at the top, removed several crisp bills and handed them to Helen, along with the advice to, "Get things practical, but winsome too: outfits, shoes, stockings and under pretties. I trust your judgment."

Helen departed and Marge again turned her attention to Red, saying, "Peter says you lost your parents. I'm so sorry."

"Yes," Red said. "Thank you."

Marge went on. "Mark my words, everything is going to be fine. A friend of mine, Mrs. Damon, has been looking for a nanny. It is a position tailor-made for you. Until then, I want you to stay here. I think you will find the accommodations quite satisfactory. The bed in your room has a glorious feather mattress, soft but firm. I've never had a guest complain.

"During your stay, I would prefer you remain on this floor. It would be best for you not to disturb our other guests. And if you hear music, or laughter and merriment, think nothing of it. Sometimes our guests like to have fun."

Curiosity got the best of Red. "Is this a hotel?"

Without hesitation Marge replied, "Yes it is." She went on to say, "I put a few magazines on the nightstand for you, and also a copy of Emily Post's book, *Etiquette*. It tells about correct social behavior. I want you to study it. It will prove extremely beneficial to you in your life. Let me ask you, do you enjoy Will Rogers?"

"I heard him on the radio," Red said and it seemed to her that her voice was suddenly very small and inconsequential.

"He is a wonderful humorist," Marge continued. "I absolutely love his homespun philosophy and the way he makes a mockery of our politicians. I cut out several of his columns from the newspaper and put them on your nightstand."

There was a knock at the door and Marge asked Red, "Would you please answer that?"

Red opened the door and found a cart with linen, silver tea service and china cups.

"Please, bring it in, darling."

While they sipped tea, the conversation continued with Marge taking charge and Red mostly answering questions. Marge talked to her, not as a child, but as an adult.

"You will like working for Mrs. Damon. She has a very handsome home. Of course you will have to prove yourself, show you can do the work and care for her child. I believe she only has the one."

"What will I be doing?"

"A nanny does a little of everything, but primarily you will be responsible for the child's welfare: changing diapers, dressing, naps, and laundry. All those things a mother does.

"But now we must get you ready to try on your new clothes. Go to your room, get out of what you are wearing and take a nice, leisurely bath. When you have finished, put on the robe that is there for you. I'll call for you when Helen returns."

◌◌◌◌◌◌◌

Wrapped in the white robe, Red returned to Marge's room to find a wonderful array of packages open and waiting her inspection. Helen said, "Try this on first. It's absolutely adorable."

Red, who was most comfortable wearing trousers, flannel shirt and work boots, looked over the gray pleated wool skirt, peach colored blouse, white stockings, saddle shoes, silk camisole and matching bra and panties laid out over a chair. She had never even touched silk. She was shy about undressing in front of the two women and Marge took notice and offered, "Why don't you change in my bedroom." She motioned toward a door.

Red closed the door behind her and slipped on the panties, bra and silk camisole. She marveled at how soft and luxurious the material felt against her skin. She ran one finger between her breasts and then all four fingers traced a course across her

43

flat stomach. She pulled on the skirt, smoothed it over her legs and felt a delicious tingle of pleasure race through her body. By the time she finished dressing, her shyness had dissolved. She materialized from the bedroom twirling lightheartedly on her tiptoes. From under the skirt flashed glimpses of long legs and knobby knees. She glowed with strength, good health and youthful vitality. And in that moment, she was absolutely sure her new life was going to be everything her old life had not been: pleasurable, entertaining, thrilling, happy, carefree and grand.

Later, after she had taken her new clothes to her room, the same colored woman whom she had seen on the second floor landing knocked on the door and asked for Red's old clothes. As she handed them over she inquired, "Are you fixin' to wash them?"

The colored lady never changed her expression. "Mrs. Davenport directed they be burned."

That afternoon Helen spent nearly an hour combing, cutting and curling Red's hair. She even gave instructions on makeup, adding simple touches here and there. When Marge knocked on the door, Red was wearing a scarlet dress with matching shoes. Her hair hung in curly ringlets. Marge gave her an approving smile and said, "You're as cute as a bug's ear."

Red walked downstairs with her hostess, trying to remember if anyone had ever before paid her a compliment on her physical appearance. She did not think so. They reached the dining room and the surprises continued. Seven lovely ladies were seated at the long table awaiting their arrival. All the ladies were beautiful and no two looked alike. Some had bobbed hair and others wore their hair long. As a whole, the group appeared to be women of good breeding with expensive tastes in clothing.

Marge motioned for Red to sit at an open seat while she assumed the chair at the head of the table. She sat, bowed her head, said grace and offered a short prayer of thanks for bringing "this new little bird to our doorstep." She glanced at Red and smiled serenely. The others closed the prayer with, "Amen."

The women exhibited sterling table manners with "please pass" and "thank you" sprinkled here and there as they dabbled in wide-ranging conversations touching on diverse subjects: politics, investments, automobiles they favored and the many gay parties they had attended. Red watched the others and learned which utensil to use, how to eat and the proper way for her to conduct herself. While she dined, it crossed her mind that these women were either movie stars or maybe—she had seen the word in one of her friend Zelda's Hollywood magazines, but it did not come immediately to her mind—then she remembered the word was *debutantes*. She concluded the hotel was reserved for young women about to make their entrance into high society.

Dessert was fresh peach cobbler with whipped cream. Red indulged herself, and as she spooned a bite of the rich and sweetly delicious treat into her mouth, she overheard Helen discretely whisper to one of the other ladies, "Whom are you seeing this evening?"

"I have the senator at seven and Mr. Livingston at nine. He is new, quite charming and very, very wealthy. Most likely he will choose to spend the night."

"Girls," Marge scolded. "Must I remind you, appropriate table talk never involves matters of a business?"

After dinner, Red returned to her room to read the book on etiquette. She fell asleep reading and awoke hearing music emanating from downstairs. On a whim, she decided to investigate. She pulled the robe over her pajamas and walked

45

barefooted down the plush carpeted stairs, taking a seat near the bottom where it would be difficult for anyone in the big room to see her.

From this vantage, she watched two debutantes dancing with a pair of well-dressed gentlemen. She overheard the blonde, who had sat beside her at dinner say, "You must be getting warm." She helped the man remove his suit coat and hung it neatly over the back of a chair. They resumed dancing, holding each other tightly, moving together to the slow beat of the music. Before long the blonde whispered something in the gentleman's ear and he enthusiastically agreed. The blonde took his arm and began to lead him toward the staircase. Red reacted decisively, ducking around the corner to avoid being seen. A few minutes later the other couple in the room followed suit, ascending the stairs to rooms on the second floor.

Peeking around the corner, Red watched the second couple step onto the landing, where they paused for a long intimate embrace. It was in that precise moment the many clues added up to something in Red's mind: the spacious house, the imposing gate, the uniformed doorman, the elaborate furnishings, the beautiful and expensively attired women, the dinner conversation about a man spending the night, the gentlemen visitors, the way the dancers clung to each other, and finally their embrace on the landing.

She suddenly had a vague sense she was not alone, turned her head slightly and saw Helen standing only a few feet away.

"You shouldn't be spying on people."

"I wasn't, really. I just needed a little fresh air."

"Ah-huh."

Red blurted, "Are you chippies?" It was a word her friend Bertie had used to describe women of questionable virtue.

"No," Helen said, her voice as strained as if filtered through brittle shards of glass. "A chippie is a low-class woman who sells herself cheaply and indiscriminately."

"What are you then?"

"Whores. We have sophistication, are paid handsomely to bring pleasure to men, and earn our money honestly. There's nothing wrong with being a whore."

⋯⋯⋯⋯

Away from the city, away from people and traffic and the constant rumble of noise and activity, the night stars appeared luminescent, clear and steady. Moisture from the ocean settled on the rich land, covering the blades of verdant grasses with fresh dew. When the moon finally did appear it bathed the foothills—rounded and woman-like—in a soft and sensual blush. The lonely world drew in a long, cool collective breath and went about the process of renewing itself.

Chapter Five

Dear Mother,

Thought you ought to know there was an accident. Lost my leg, the left one, a little below the knee. But I'm on the mend and the doc says I'm pretty near healed. They're giving me a new leg today and after I practice a bit, should get around no problem.

I know this comes as a shock. I'm sorry to upset you. It was just one of those accidents that happen.

I'll write again. Give my love to Nellie and little Donny. Again, I'm sorry.

Your Loving Son,

Jack

P.S. If you see Kelsey around, tell him I'm doing fine and headed west to California.

After the swelling had subsided in Jack's injured leg, a plaster mold was made of his stump and sent to a wood carver in Reno to whittle the prosthesis. While Jack waited, dark memories emerged, so distant and foreign they might have been lived by someone else. He recalled a specific night when his family lived in Denver. It was only a few months after his mother married her second husband, Frank Steinman. Awakened by a heated exchange, Jack crawled out of bed, made his way across the dark room and cracked open the door. If his mother had chanced a look she would have seen her son's face bisected, half bathed in light and the other in shadow.

Nellie came awake, stood in her crib shaking the bars and making baby noises. He pushed the door shut for a moment and told her, "Shhh," before returning his attention to the front room. Grace stood with hands on her hips confronting Frank.

"I will not allow your mother to move in here with us, not under this roof. The kids are already doubled up. We barely have room for the four of us."

Frank had his feet firmly planted. "Don't backtalk me. You're my wife. Do as I say."

Grace jabbed a stiff index finger at Frank's breastbone. Her words were as sharp-edged and dangerous as a hunk of obsidian, "Over my dead body."

Frank began to turn away, but abruptly changed his mind. In an effort to intimidate Grace with his sheer size, he moved even closer. She refused to cower. He raised his hand and snarled, "You bitch. I'll have this marriage annulled like it never happened."

"You call this a marriage? Go ahead, get your annulment." Grace defiantly threw back her head, sending her long hair flying. "I must have been completely desperate to have married you. I certainly never loved you."

With that ugly truth revealed, Frank Steinman marched out the door, never to return. In the aftermath of that short and disastrous marriage, Grace kept her family together by taking an array of odd jobs: babysitting neighborhood children, cleaning houses, and clerking in a department store through the Christmas season. But even though she worked hard, there came one month when she could not make the rent. She wrote the landlord a letter of apology, promising to pay as soon as she was able. A few days later a process server appeared at the door with a notice of eviction. She had no alternative but to pack as many worldly possessions as she could cram into a single, well-worn leather grip and move out. With children in tow, she hiked to a nearby cafe where she took a booth with an unobstructed view of the street.

Sipping hot Brazilian coffee from a glass mug, she absently watched a storm build and send drops of rain boomeranging into puddles on the street. She told herself she had to find a place for her and her children to live and momentarily entertained a notion that perhaps she should swallow her pride and return to her parents' home in Chicago. But she remembered the scene when her father found out she was pregnant with Jack, and not yet married. He berated her saying she had brought shame to the family name, and from that day forward she was no longer his daughter. Perhaps enough time had passed, and the old wounds had healed. No, she told herself, she could not crawl home with two kids and a pair of failed marriages. Never.

By the time she finished her fourth cup of coffee her heart was racing and a few lingering clouds were busy scudding eastward. The sun arced into an opening of blue sky and sunlight splayed great bars of alabaster light in perfectly symmetrical rays. Hopeful reflections bounced off the flat sheen of puddles and passing traffic threw up a mist that turned into a lovely rainbow.

She paid for her coffee and Jack's hot chocolate and took her family into the street. One hand clutched the grip and she used the free hand to balance Nellie on her hip. Jack shuffled along a step or two behind. They walked to Broadway where they found people gathered on the sidewalk intently listening to a man standing on an overturned apple crate.

The moment Grace laid eyes on this man—he wore tailored slacks, a suit coat, and a short-brimmed felt hat pushed back away from his handsome face—she was smitten. This stranger communicated an air of self-righteous confidence, superiority and charm. Grace refused, or maybe she was not capable of recognizing, that a man with so much power could easily dominate her, consume her. She stood there in a silly fog mesmerized by the man's words that flowed as smoothly as warm honey.

"How many of you struggle in your lives?" he asked. "I would venture to guess each and every one of us struggles at one time or another. But no matter how far down we get we always have the opportunity to lend a helping hand to our fellow man. Charity begins and ends on a personal level. We each possess that innate ability to facilitate good and to make a real difference in the lives of those around us.

"Why, not long ago I saw a group of children sitting in front of a tarpaper shack. They had holes in their britches and were underfed. I knew in my heart I must do something to alleviate their sad plight. I stopped and spoke with them. Their mother came to the door and told me a heart-wrenching tale of woe, of how her husband had died and left her and the children without any source of income. They were destitute and without hope.

"I went to church that Sunday, prayed for the woman, and then I told her story to the congregation. On her behalf I begged for food, clothing and furniture. The people responded, giving from the bottom of their hearts, and in fact so much was donated I had to borrow a truck to take all the gifts to this needy family.

"Their cupboards overflowed, the closets were jam-packed, and the bug-infested pallets on the floor where the children slept were replaced with beds. That day, as I left their home, I was filled with personal pride for spearheading the drive to help these wonderful folks get back on their feet.

"The next time I was in the neighborhood I stopped to visit and was astounded to find the children once again sleeping on the floor. I asked what had happened to the beds and one of the children replied, 'Mommy gave them away to some really poor people.'

"Ladies and gentlemen, this clearly demonstrates that no matter how bad off you think you might be at the moment, there is always someone worse off than you. In closing, I would like to leave you with one lasting thought—if you give to others, God will bless you tenfold. Thank you very much. And now please feel free to contribute to the cause."

As the speaker stepped into the crowd he removed his hat, turned it upside down and thrust it, first at those who appeared especially well-heeled, and then at anyone within reach. The gathering quickly dispersed until only Grace and her children remained. When he realized no additional money would be forthcoming he removed the money from his hat, tucked it in his pocket and replaced the hat on his head.

"Sir, your speech was so very inspirational and moving. Thank you for sharing your message about giving," Grace said.

"Glad you enjoyed it" he replied with a ready smile.

For some odd reason, unknown even to Grace, she found herself wanting to confide in this street preacher. Perhaps she anticipated he would come to her aid as he had for the destitute family. She said, "I find myself in a similar situation as the one you described, without a husband, penniless, with children to look after. I don't know how we will survive."

"Care for a cup of coffee?" he offered.

The last thing Grace wanted was more coffee, but she graciously accepted the invitation. They went to a nearby diner, sipped drinks and talked while Jack fell asleep using his mother's leg as a pillow.

The man introduced himself as Chester Harmon. "But please call me Chet."

Chet listened as she told about leaving her first husband and the terrible mistake she had made with the second. He confided he wanted to become an actor and felt his impromptu speeches on downtown street corners were preparing him for his eventual career in the movies.

"One of these days, silent movies will be a thing of the past. They'll have movies that talk. You will be able to hear the actors speak. I have the perfect voice, and once I have perfected my acting skills, the sky will be the limit."

And when the discussion finally came around to her immediate situation, it was Chet who proposed she temporarily place the children in what he referred to as "a special home." He said he knew of a place that would take children on a temporary basis. "It's operated by the Catholic Church and is located just south of the State Capitol on Sixth Avenue."

Grace was horrified by his suggestion. "I could never give up my children."

"Temporarily, only temporarily." The tone of his voice became compassionate. "You have to have faith that what you do now will be in the best interests of your children in the long run. In such a home, children are well cared for and loved, and you give yourself the opportunity to get back on your feet."

Grace went from being adamantly opposed to giving up her children to eventually viewing the notion as a tiny glimmer of hope in a world of dark depression. Still she rebelled. "I couldn't. People would say I abandoned them."

His fingers closed around her delicate wrist. "My dear, you cannot be concerned with what people say. Always remember, the best weapon against a lie is truth. I do not know of any weapon against gossip, but I do know, for fact, gossip is like the fog. A good west wind whisks it away and warm sun dissolves it. So, you only need satisfy yourself that such a temporary situation would be in the best interest of you and your family."

"Thank you. You have been very understanding."

While she contemplated her next course of action, he sat across from her and tried to exploit the situation to his best advantage. He soothed the young woman's pain with words—*selflessness, opportunity, concern,* and *love*—and while he talked the waitresses moved efficiently about the room and customers came and went. Nellie awoke and slept again. Jack snored lightly.

┼┼┼┼┼┼

Jack woke up feeling slightly nauseous. He had recovered by the time his wooden prosthesis arrived on the 8:45 train from Reno. The doctor brought it to Jack's room, and after making a few slight alterations to the cup of the prosthesis using his pocket knife and sandpaper, he fiddled with the straps and belt, secured it in place and asked Jack to try standing.

"Is that comfortable?"

Jack knew the device would never be comfortable, but nodded his acceptance. The doctor departed and Jack practiced the routine of easing his stump into the socket opening, affixing the strap and belt as he had been shown, and finally, with difficulty, tugging his trousers over his prosthesis. During this process, he got it in his head—actually it was a gnawing feeling in his gut—he wanted to go home. More than anything he yearned to be consoled by his mother.

He made an unsteady escape from the hospital, limping to the Elko rail yard where he sat on a little knoll and watched cars being loaded with three-year-old steers fresh off the Nevada range. As the train pulled away, he screwed up his courage and hobbled to a boxcar in front of the stock cars where the Nevada cattle bellowed their annoyance and shoved rank green scum through the openings between the slats. Using arm strength mostly, and a little hop from his good leg, he successfully propelled himself aboard the eastbound freight. For a while he laid on his back, stretched across the wood floor, breathing hard, heart pounding, a tingle of raw fear and exhilaration coursing through him. He closed his eyes, concentrated on the rumble of the drive wheels digging for traction, and the rattle, shake and other tangible evidence of acceleration. All the familiar noises returned: the rhythmic clickity-clack of wheels charging over joints in the rails, the screeching of metal grinding against metal, the smell of hot grease, and the distant rumble of the powerful locomotive. The rocking and swaying caused by uneven rails and the residue of burning coal were strangely soothing. Even after his horrific accident, the train did not bring him fear, instead he welcomed all the familiar sights, sounds, smells, sensations and impressions of the moving train as if they were old friends whom he remembered fondly and had missed.

He told himself that the few short weeks he had spent as a carefree hobo, going wherever the rails and a passing train happened to carry him, had been the best times of his young life. Now he managed a tight-lipped grin because he had won back his independence. The euphoria was soon replaced by the monotony of the ride. His thoughts turned to his family;

his mother first and foremost, and then his brother and sister. Finally, as the full effect of darkness pressed in, he wrestled with the painful and ugly details of arriving home and facing his stepfather, Chet Harmon.

⌗⌗⌗⌗⌗⌗

On the night of his accident, an image of Chet had come to Jack. The family was in his automobile. He was driving and turned and flashed a reassuring smile in Grace's direction as he braked and pulled to the curb. She, with Nellie in her arms, stepped out. She nodded to Jack, who was in the back seat, that he was to follow her.

The three of them stood in a tight little group on the sidewalk. Chet leaned across the seat and spoke through the open window, "I'll pull ahead into the shade and wait for you."

The family made its way up a series of steps leading to an austere gray stone building. A sign over the double doors declared *Our Lady of the Forgiving Heart Welfare and Orphanage Home*. Grace hesitated. She took a deep breath, exhaled and then lifted the knocker and tapped three distinct times. One of the doors opened, creaking on brass hinges. Standing in the twilight of the interior was a sizable woman dressed in a hooded black-and-white habit. The woman stepped forward, took Jack's hands in hers and in an even, reassuring tone said, "I am Sister Elizabeth. You must be Jack. You and I will have a fine time together."

Jack stood unmoving, except for his eyes that had widened as he looked up into the face of Sister Elizabeth. She had a dark brown mole on the right side of her face, a thin stand of brown mustache hair on her upper lip and a bluish tinge to her skin, as if her body temperature was visibly cooler than a normal person. She bent at the waist and pulled him against her ample bosom. She smelled of sweet French soap and fresh peppermint toothpaste.

Sister Elizabeth abruptly released him, stood and turned all her attention to Nellie. "What a perfect baby," she cooed. "Yes, you are. Perfect. Perfect. Perfect in every way."

He watched Sister Elizabeth take Nellie and saw a dreadful sadness come to his mother's eyes as she rubbed her empty hands together in an effort to keep her childless fingers busy. The line of her mouth turned grim, hard set and determined. Then she kissed Nellie, planted a corresponding kiss on Jack's forehead, turned, and with quick deliberate strides descended the stairs. She marched directly to Chet's automobile. As she drew near, he leaned across the seat and opened the door for her.

If his mother had explained to Jack this was to be a temporary situation—that she would return for him and Nellie just as soon as she was able—then perhaps he could have understood and maybe even accepted her desertion. Instead, his young mind could comprehend only that his mother was abandoning him and his sister too.

He allowed Sister Elizabeth, with Nellie in the crook of one arm, to lead him through the doorway. Other nuns appeared, gathered around and made a noisy fuss over Nellie while Jack remained on the fringe. Before long he was taken to the basement where other children were playing with blocks and dolls and rolling rubber balls to each other. He was the newcomer. No one welcomed him. He crossed the room. The pattern on the floor alternated between white and black tile. He went to a bookshelf, selected a book, sat on the floor and opened it.

Sister Elizabeth came to him. "Are you looking at pictures?"

He shook his head.

"Would you like to learn to read?"

"I already know how. Mommy taught me." His voice was defiant.

"Read that page for me."

Jack read haltingly, as if each word were a separate sentence. "Jesus - loves - me - this - I - know." He rolled onto his side and propped himself on an elbow. "But I don't believe Jesus loves me."

"What makes you say such a dreadful thing?"

"If He loved me, He wouldn't let Mommy leave."

                            :::::::::

It was unusual for boys to spend more than a few days at *Our Lady of the Forgiving Heart*. There was a waiting list of farmers eager to adopt boys. Farmers always needed boys to work the fields, especially when the only pay was room and board. But Jack was not eligible for release until he had been a resident a minimum of 90 days.

Other boys, in normal homes, were running barefooted through tall grasses where field mice hid and quail flushed in a flurry of wing beats. Other boys were swinging on long ropes and dropping into the cool water of a swimming hole. Other boys got to fish, ride stick horses and play cowboys and Indians in the great outdoors. Not Jack, confined as he was, he was not like other boys.

                            :::::::::

Across the street from the orphanage was a low-slung farmhouse, a leftover from a past era when that section of town had been rural. The old couple living there still kept farm animals, including a flock of chickens. The hens doted over several batches of fuzzy yellow chicks, keeping them away from the sporadic automobile traffic and safe from the occasional dog that wandered through.

From his time spent doing chores in the kitchen, Jack knew where the cook kept a sack of oatmeal. He stole a cupful. He went to the far fence, flung a small handful and coaxed the chickens into the street. He never purposely intended to lure the baby chicks into range in order to harm them, but when they ventured near, and finding he was holding a rock in his hand, he mechanically cocked his arm and threw the rock. The rock hit one of the chicks, crushing its paper-thin skull. It fluttered for a moment and then lay motionless, its long neck stretched at an odd angle against the hard-packed roadway.

The chicks and hens, which temporarily scattered, returned to the oatmeal. They ignored their fallen comrade and once again began pecking at the offering. Jack threw another rock and missed. The third rock hit a chick in the chest. It flopped onto its back and kicked its spindly legs in the throes of death. Jack found himself caught up in the excitement of killing, never pausing to examine the consequences, as tiny yellow bodies began to litter the road like so many delicate daffodils battered by a cruel spring hailstorm. All that mattered to him was that he held dominance, and his power was absolute. His inner pain at his abandonment dissolved.

The telephone rang and Grace answered. She talked very little, mostly she listened. Even after the line went dead she remained with the receiver cocked to one ear. What disturbed her was how suddenly the tenuous balance of her relationship with Chet was being threatened. She thought he was close, oh so very close to proposing. She finally hung up the receiver and reluctantly returned to the table.

"Who was that?" A quick glance at her troubled expression caused Chet to rephrase the question, "Is everything all right?"

She sighed, bit her lower lip and searched for just the right words, settling for, "No, everything is not all right." Then, rather than say Jack had been accused of killing baby chicks and was being expelled from the orphanage, she told a little white lie. "The nuns say they don't have room for the children and they want me to pick them up."

Chet got up from his chair, came and kissed her on her forehead. Then, with one finger on her chin, he tilted her head upward. He said, "As of late I've been giving matters considerable thought. I do believe, maybe, we should...." He laughed. "That's not exactly how I had it planned." He dropped to one knee, took her limp hands in his and requested, "Grace, my darling, will you marry me?"

A justice of the peace married the couple the following day. The only witness to the short civil ceremony was a woman who had come to the courthouse to pay a fine. On their way home, Chet stopped at *Our Lady of the Forgiving Heart Welfare and Orphanage Home* and Grace picked up the children.

Chapter Six

Red soon moved out of Marge's mansion and into another mansion, this one owned by Daniel and Antoinette Damon. Red had been hired to serve as the couple's live-in nanny for their son, one-year-old Anthony.

Mrs. Damon was much younger than her influential, international banker husband and thought of herself as a woman of culture and refinement. It quickly became evident that she had hired Red to be a surrogate mother while she played the role of social queen bee, buzzing about the finest homes in the hills of San Francisco and attending lively parties in the hallowed ballrooms of elite hotels. Mrs. Damon usually attended these events on the arm of a handsome young man, chosen from a stable of men she kept for that express purpose.

Mr. Damon, who had been born into a New York banking family, spent most of his time on the East Coast. When he was in the Bay Area he could be found at one of the many gentlemen's clubs where he held membership: Pacific Union, Olympic, Union League or the University Club. Here, despite Prohibition, he drank without fear of arrest and conducted his business affairs with men of equal stature. Whenever the mood or need struck, he visited a house such as the one Marge Davenport owned and operated in the Tenderloin.

The Damons insisted on addressing Red as Miss Mavis. When Mr. or Mrs. Damon returned home they often requested, "Miss Mavis, please bring me the child." No matter what was going on at that particular moment, even if the baby was sleeping, Red was expected to produce Anthony in a timely manner. He was to be awake, clean and impeccably dressed. After a few minutes of interaction with the child, Red was called on to whisk Anthony away. If Mrs. Damon had been the one to issue the summons, she usually braced herself with vodka on the rocks and a twist of lime. The few times Mr. Damon made a request, he promptly turned his attention to a tall glass of twelve-year-old blended Scotch.

Red's quarters were adjacent to Anthony's room and linked by an adjoining door. For the first few weeks of her employment, Red was thrilled with the arrangement and thought she was extremely lucky to be living in the lap of luxury and enjoying all the conveniences available to the wealthy. She could hardly believe she had acquired such a lofty position that paid, in addition to room and board, the handsome sum of $3 a week.

However, she was on call seven days a week. Her only recreation was to push Anthony in his baby carriage through the neighborhood. In their wanderings they visited various parks where Red sat and watched pigeons land on statues of dead dignitaries, depositing droppings that eventually turned the stone as pale as ghosts. When they were alone, Red called the baby Tony. She loved the little boy—his brown hair, hazel eyes, and his quick and terrific smile—and since the parents had such little contact with their son, Red began to think of the child as her own. Sometimes she told people she met in parks or on the street, that Tony was her son.

Red felt it was her duty to protect Tony from his hobnobbing mother and her constant bouts with the bottle. The situation became more tenuous when Mr. Damon began showing up more often, and if his wife was out, he made clumsy passes at Red. He claimed he found her *appealing, alluring,* and *quite tempting.* He told her, "There is a winsome quality about you that I find enormously seductive."

On October 29, 1929, the stock market collapsed. Within a few short hours the rich suddenly got a taste of what it was like to be poor. Red knew nothing about the event, nor could she have ever envisioned the worldwide financial devastation it would cause. That evening, when both Mr. and Mrs. Damon arrived home within minutes of each other, Red assumed they would want to see their son. She dressed him in a cute red jumpsuit, but when she brought the child to the living room she found Mr. Damon seated on one end of the sofa, head buried in his hands. He looked up and his cheeks were wet with tears. Mrs. Damon, who was seated at the opposite end of the sofa from her husband, snapped at Red, "Leave us alone. Can't you see we're having a conversation?"

Later that evening, one of the maids filled Red in on the news and the effects it would most likely have on the Damon household. She told Red, "What it means is 'fore the week's out everyone who works here is gonna be out on the street. The cow has done gone dry."

The following day—and what was especially odd was that Red spent all day in the house and never heard a thing—the maid with whom Red had spoken to the night before discovered Mr. Damon's body. He had gone into his study, taken his twelve-gauge shotgun from the gun safe, loaded a shell in the chamber, placed the end of the barrel in his mouth and pulled the trigger. Even before the funeral arrangements had been made, most of the staff was sent away. Red, in addition to her duties of caring for Anthony, was expected to pick up the slack and do everything the maid and others had done—cleaning, washing, ironing and cooking.

Mrs. Damon set a steady course to drink away the sad reality that she had been left a penniless widow. Within the week her parents came from Boise, Idaho, to rescue her. They packed her personal belongings, gathered Anthony's clothes and toys and as they were leaving, Mrs. Damon's father said to Red, "Your services are no longer required. Please vacate the premises."

Red was not quite 16 years old, and with her limited educational background and lack of work experience, there was little chance for her finding employment. She felt her only redemption rested in Marge's capable hands. She wondered if Marge would be so generous a second time around.

On the taxi ride uptown, she recalled how impressed she had been with the big houses, the fancy architecture and the overall vitality of the Tenderloin. But since Wall Street's collapse, the area had quickly fallen on hard times. Businesses were boarded up, garbage littered the sidewalks, very few automobiles prowled the streets and unemployed men stood idly on street corners.

The taxi driver stopped in front of Marge's elaborate front gate. A uniformed guard—a man Red did not recognize—spoke with her, asked several questions and relayed the information through the intercom. Marge's voice replied over the speaker, "Send her up. She knows the way."

After exchanging small talk with Marge, Red came to the point of her visit. She asked for employment. A slow smile began to spread across Marge's face.

"What can you do for me?"

"Anything."

Marge's smile broadened, "Anything? You want to be one of my painted ladies?"

"I could if that's the only opening you have."

Marge unfastened the lid of her ornate gold case, plucked a cigarette, lit it and blew out a thin stream of white smoke.

"Sweetie, no woman starts life with her sights set on becoming a whore. It's a path seldom chosen because, in the end, a girl squanders her beauty and most of her good years.

"I've been in this business 40 years and seen hundreds of girls come and go. I have educated each and every one. I've trained them to become knowledgeable on a wide range of subjects, to behave as well-mannered ladies, and have provided them the opportunities to use their God-given assets to make a handsome living for themselves.

"I am a doctor administering first aid and do-it-yourself gynecology. I am a psychologist working to understand the female mind and mood. I am a coach taking a group of individuals and molding them into a winning team that does not fight or bicker.

"Out of necessity I have learned a dozen remedies to sober a man enough so he can leave and go home to his wife. I've developed a fair-to-middling grasp of what it takes to drive a pimp away because, whenever a girl is making money there are always scurrilous men wanting to steal the chattel. And I have learned the business side of sex, whom I need to pay and when to pay them.

"What has this vast accumulation of knowledge and skills gained me? Society brands me with a scarlet letter. I am a whorehouse madam. There are those who claim my business is immoral. As far as I am concerned morality is nothing more than a particular word in vogue with a particular society at a particular point in time. I provide this city with a social service. Each customer comes here of his own free will. He alone is the one who makes the determination whether or not he wishes to pay to play.

"Men come for sex, but they also come to talk about their problems, to discover a new thrill to spice up their lives, have an honest drink, a bite of good food, and intelligent conversation with someone pretty and charming who will laugh at their dull-witted jokes. But most of all, men come here for a few fleeting moments of what they view as intimacy.

"Years ago I lost count of the women who have come to my door asking for employment. Most were clearly unfit for the task. They were too young or too old, too loose, too cheap, too plain, or too dull. If a girl is down on her luck and comes to me I might give her money to tide her over. If she wants to work for me I generally offer this bit of advice: *stay the hell out of the pleasure-giving business.* I only have need for a true professional—a lady who genuinely wants to pleasure a man for money."

Marge ground out her cigarette in an ashtray and turned her attention back to Red.

"I would be willing to wager you have never been with a man."

"I can learn."

Marge cackled and coughed. "Sugar, take it from me, you're not suited for this line of work."

But Marge did offer Red a place to stay until she could locate another job. Red declined. A taxi was called and Red used some of her savings to rent a room at a hotel. She whiled away her idle time—all she had was idle time—by going to movies. One afternoon she called Peter to see if he wanted to go to a movie with her. He declined, saying he could not afford the gas to get there, or the dime for the matinee.

Finally, when Red's limited savings were nearly depleted, she was forced to look for work and luckily found a job as a house servant for Florien Tierney, an elderly woman suffering with terminal cancer. Florien was a spiteful woman, unwilling to suffer alone. Any time of the day or night, whenever she rang the little bell at her bedside, Red was expected to tend any real or imagined discomfort Florien might be suffering; from fetching a glass of water, to turning Florien on her side, or emptying her bedpan.

Occasionally, a friend of Florien's came to visit, and then for a few blessed hours Red could escape. She lived for those moments of freedom because the sick woman reminded Red of how terrible it had been caring for her own mother the last months of her life. It seemed to Red that, as far back as the flu epidemic that claimed her father, illness in those near her had been a constant companion.

Red was stealing a few hours of freedom. She sat on a rock wall overlooking the city and San Francisco Bay, remembering the day of her father's funeral. He was a popular man and bar patrons, homesteaders and farmers from the surrounding area attended the service. They were escorted by wives who made the most of the day by loading up on groceries and supplies while their kids roamed town, gathering in clusters like packs of stray dogs.

The long funeral procession for Marvin—composed mostly of wagons, buckboards and buggies, as well as a few farm trucks and automobiles—passed near a group of kids standing on Main Street. Red quickly looked away from them. She knew she would never again feel carefree like her classmates did.

The caravan ascended Cemetery Hill and Red watched limber squirrels jump from branch to branch in the big elm trees; also taking notice of the horses and cows in the fields that were losing their shiny hair and putting on shaggy winter coats. She dabbed at her eyes with a handkerchief because her daddy would never see any of this, never watch the grass grow, river flow, wind blow. He was dead and he was never coming back.

The driver pulled back on the lines, stopping the team of matched blacks. He set the brake and helped Ann and Red from the buggy. Peter climbed down and the three stood together while six husky men maneuvered the casket into position. Overhead a black cloud worked to gobble up the sky as slanting rays of sunlight forced the stubble fields below to radiate a flat metallic sheen. A cold north wind sprang to life, blowing ripples of dust across the hardpan, drifting yellow leaves, and sending tumbleweeds skittering playfully across the terrain. The air, dry and dusty, made Red's nostrils sting and she wrinkled her nose to breathe easier. Her mother reached down and took hold of her hand. The preacher began to speak.

Without warning, a blue lance shot from the seething cloud overhead. Almost instantaneously thunder cracked and rolled, echoing back and forth across the undulating hills. Then another quiver of light, and again the corresponding crash. The air shook with the impact of colliding forces. The preacher stopped talking. People hurried away from the gravesite, leaving only the family and two men off to the side resting on their shovel handles.

Ann asked Red, "Are you alright?"

"I'm fine, Mommy."

"Your daddy was a good man."

"I know, Mommy."

"Are you ready to go?"

"Yes."

That evening Red went to bed early. She lay there repeating one word over and over again—bug, bug, bug, bug, bug, bug, bug. It sounded so funny that she began to laugh. A moment later she thought about her father lying there on that windswept hill and began to cry because she didn't know how she could ever forgive herself for never telling him goodbye or saying, one last time, "I love you, Daddy."

In the morning, Red got up from bed, went downstairs and found her mother sitting at the kitchen table with Mr. Thurman, the family attorney. They were talking in quiet voices. Ann looked up, saw her daughter and managed a tight-lipped smile. She opened her arms, and when Red came to her, she pulled her daughter onto her lap. Mr. Thurman, obviously not wanting to waste time, continued to talk, saying, "I'm sorry to tell you this, but Marvin never finalized his will."

Ann knew Mr. Thurman was being dishonest and challenged him. "I thought when he sent for you there near the end, he wanted you to write his will."

"True enough." Then Mr. Thurman twisted the truth. "But he wanted me to take it back to the office, type it up official-like and then he said he'd sign it. But he never did. He died before I could get back to him."

"What's going to happen?"

"We revert to his former will naming Ed Hall as his beneficiary. That was done for business reasons, since they were business partners. But rest assured, Mrs. Durkee, I will make sure you get everything you legally have coming to you, although I'm not sure it's much. Your farm carries a heavy mortgage."

"The saloon. Surely there's money there."

"Since Prohibition was ratified, it made the manufacture, or sale, of alcoholic drinks illegal. The saloon operated in violation of that law. Local officials were bought off. But after Marvin's passing the doors were locked."

In the days and weeks after the funeral, Peter became the sole breadwinner for the family. He continued to do odd jobs at Mr. Logan's store, as well as running a trapline along the Yellowstone River, bringing home muskrat and mink that he skinned on the kitchen floor and stretched the hides on drying boards. He hunted the nearby fields and hills for rabbits and squirrels and the family ate wild game at nearly every meal.

Red did what she could. She hauled firewood, one chunk at a time, from the woodshed to the box by the kitchen stove. She helped her mother with chores, but the barn never felt as comforting to her as it had when her father was alive. She merely went through the motions of gathering eggs, and feeding the animals while her mother milked the cow.

Once a week, on Wednesday, Red and her mother washed clothes. Rather than carry water from the spring to the house, it was much easier to take the clothes to the spring where an iron wash boiler was perched on a foundation of rocks. They built a hot fire, and after the clothes were boiled they were scrubbed on the washboard, rinsed in spring water, and carried to the clothesline and hung to dry. On the coldest days the moisture froze and ice had to be shaken from the garments.

Ann sewed trousers for Peter from old coats and dresses for Red from flour sacks. She baked bread on Sunday. She worked hard because there was no other choice but to work hard. Without an income, they had to make do. And they did, raising what they could and selling cream, eggs and an occasional hog or steer for spending money.

Those nights when Ann could not sleep—and there were many—she sat by the fire and worked on a wedding ring quilt. When it was finished, she took it into town and sold it to the banker's wife, using the money she was paid to buy garden seeds. "If you don't grow it in the summer and can it in the fall, there won't be anything to eat come winter," she explained to her children. That spring they had a big garden with lots of peas, beans, radishes, and carrots. Later they harvested potatoes, corn and squash.

It was just before the bulk of the garden was ready to harvest that the sheriff paid a visit, brusquely rapping his knuckles on the screen door. Ann, drying her hands on her apron, answered the door to find Sheriff Watson holding a fistful of folded papers in his right hand. He said, "I know, what with the loss of Marvin, it ain't been easy for you. I hate like hell to be the one, but it's my job to serve these here papers."

She opened the screen door enough to allow him to pass the papers through. She glanced at them quickly. "Ed Hall. He signed this? What's he got to do with it? What's he want with my farm?"

"He holds the mortgage. Anyway that's what the paperwork says. I don't know nothin' about it 'cept you got 10 days to raise the money or vacate the premises. As far as I can tell, all the I's are dotted and the T's crossed. But you might want to get an out-of-town attorney, one from Miles City or Glendive. Maybe they could help you fight this. At least they might buy you some time."

Ann watched the sheriff drive away, and as the dust began to settle, she lifted her apron to her face and cried. It took her several phone calls before Ed Hall agreed to meet and discuss the foreclosure. She wore her dark blue Sunday dress to the meeting. Red was attired in a skirt and a pale blue blouse with puffy sleeves and prints of white lambs playfully jumping over rail fences. She was informed she needed to be on her best manners. Peter refused to attend the meeting.

Ann and Red were seated in Ed Hall's conference room, and after a lengthy wait, Ed finally made his appearance. He occupied the seat, seemingly a mile away, on the far end of the table. He removed a dime cigar from his coat pocket, lit it and blew nervous smoke before addressing Red, motioning to a bowl on the table, and saying, "Have a piece of candy. Help yourself."

Red, remembering that her brother had said Mr. Hall was a thief, shook her head. "No, thank you, Mr. Hall."

"Go ahead. It's good," Ed encouraged, but when the girl made no effort to reach for the bowl, he decided to get down to the business at hand. He addressed Ann. "So, what can I do for you, Mrs. Durkee?"

At first she was hesitant and drummed her fingers on the shiny surface of the table for a long moment, before saying, "Marvin never confided his business dealings to me. I guess I've got to accept the fact you own the mortgage to our farm. Mr. Thurman said you have a legal right to take it. But that's not fair and you know it. You ain't even givin' us time to put up the garden."

Ed Hall's expression never changed.

She continued, "You and my husband were partners. He knew how to run a saloon and made you lots of money. What do I have coming from the business?"

Ed took a puff from his cigar and placed it in the ashtray. "Mrs. Durkee, you know how much I thought of Marvin. He ran an honest saloon and was well-liked by most everybody, but what with Prohibition being shoved down our throats, I had no choice but to shut down. If I didn't, the Feds would've tossed me in jail and throwed away the key. I hate like hell," he nodded in Red's direction, "please excuse the language, but there ain't nothin' to divide.

"I know these are difficult times." Ed paused for dramatic effect, or perhaps he was feeling a sharp pang of guilt. He actually surprised himself by saying, "Tell you what I'm willing to do, Mrs. Durkee. You may have the garden. Stay until harvest is over. Take whatever you please—eat it, can it, do whatever with it.

"One more thing—I happen to own a small home, the old Busby place and I'll allow you and your children to live there until such time as you get back on your feet. Then we can discuss a fair rent payment."

Ann was more convinced than ever that Ed Hall was being dishonest. She fixed him with a stare. "I want what we got coming, not handouts."

Chapter Seven

For Jack, the beginning of the end of the life he had known started late one night after he was in bed. Donny was nearby in his crib, sleeping as babies sleep, soundly and deeply. His sister Nellie was in another bedroom. When his parents began fighting, Jack got up and went to the door so he could hear and see what was happening.

Chet was at the kitchen table. Grace was directly in front of him, leaning toward him, holding back her hair with one hand and trying to keep her voice down.

"We don't have one red cent to our name. The kids and I eat rotten produce you can't sell. Then you come in here, all hours of the night, stinking of booze and perfume."

Whiskey garbled Chet's words. "I wear the pants in this goddamned family."

"No, I do. You're never here. You spend your time drinking and..." she spit out the last word with utter disgust, "whoring."

He jumped to his feet and hit her with an open hand, a glancing blow that missed her face, struck her shoulder and slipped off. She reeled back several steps, until she came up against the wall where she taunted him.

"You can't even beat your own wife."

His reaction was instantaneous, closing the distance between them with a few choppy steps and delivering a mean-spirited punch to Grace's exposed stomach. She took it, gritted her teeth and managed to squeeze out, "Is that the best you got?"

"Don't mock me! Don't dare." Chet grabbed her roughly by the hair and slammed her against the wall. She managed to block his next punch with a forearm, but her defenses buckled when Chet delivered a short left that collided against her cheekbone, opening a shallow cut below her eye. A thin, red rivulet ran down her cheek.

"Stop hitting her!" Jack's shrill voice cut apart the air in the room.

Chet whirled and raised his fist. "You want some of this, you little son of a bitch?" He pushed Jack away, not hard, but more like Jack was an irritation and not a threat.

The line had been crossed. Jack would not take any more of it; he would not take another beating and he refused to allow his mother to take one. He ran to the kitchen and pulled a butcher knife from the block. He probably would have tried to kill Chet had Grace not interceded and taken the knife away.

When Chet stuck his head into the kitchen and saw what was transpiring, he threw back his head and gave a heartless laugh. "I'll take care of you when I get back." Then he left the house.

Jack pulled away from his mother, went to his room and sat on the edge of the bed shaking and shivering while wild thoughts raced in his mind. How was he going to protect his mother? How could he when she would not allow it? She had taken the knife away. He hated to think of seeing her in the morning, with a bruise around her eye the color of a smashed plum. He wanted to kill his stepfather. He loathed the thought of ever seeing him again, of feeling the bite of his belt swung in drunken anger. He concluded his only option was to run away. He quickly gathered a few meager belongings, stuffed them into a bag and slipped out the window and into the night. The only frivolous thing he brought along was his copy of *The Great Gatsby*. He had not finished reading it and had to find out how it ended.

⬚⬚⬚⬚⬚⬚

Jack awakened Kelsey by throwing a pebble against his second-story bedroom window. Kelsey pushed open the window.

"What's up, doc?"

"I'm running away from home. Wanna come?"

Kelsey cocked his head and stared off into the dark night. His response came quickly. "I got nothin' better to do. Sure, why not? Got any money?"

"Not much. Left in kinda a hurry."

"I'll heist what I can. Give me a minute."

⬚⬚⬚⬚⬚⬚

Under the pallor of a lackluster moon, the two best friends walked along the road leading toward Grand Island. Jack, eager to put distance between himself and his mean stepfather, was only vaguely aware he was walking on the balls of his feet, leaning forward and breathing through his open mouth.

Kelsey said, "I lifted three bucks from the old man's wallet. That's all he had. How 'bout you?"

"Buck thirty-seven."

"That ain't gonna get us far."

"We'll go as far as we get an' do what we gotta do."

They carried duffel bags packed with essentials: coats, a couple changes of clothes, a blanket apiece. Kelsey wore a New

York Yankees baseball cap and Jack a brown felt hat with a floppy brim, his favorite.

"Once they figure out we're gone, they might decide to have the law fetch us back," Kelsey said. "Just our luck the sheriff comes along and drags us home to face the music. Better stay off the roads and hop a freight train. That'll be our plan."

"Which way you think we ought to head, east or west?"

"West," replied Kelsey with conviction. "I've got it laid out in my mind what we're gonna do."

"What's that?"

"We're both pretty fair athletes. I read in a magazine where movie folks are crying for good stunt men. Pay a minimum of twenty bucks a week. That's to start. On top of that, you negotiate for the stunts that have a little danger. Bonus money, that's what they call it. There's this one fellow—I forget his name, but he does stunts in most all the westerns—and he puts a grand a month in his pocket. That ain't chicken feed.

"We stop and work along the way, whenever we need to. If it takes a couple weeks, or even a month, that ain't bad. Before you know it, we'll be lounging around the movie lots in Hollywood, California, waitin' for our scenes to be shot and cameras to roll. What are they all gonna think when they see us on the movie screen?"

Jack noticed a pair of weak, unsteady lights moving in their direction. "Here comes someone. Don't suppose it's the law, do you?"

"Naw. Your old man, he don't give a shit, and mine won't get up for another five hours. Probably some poor working stiff."

The automobile had almost reached them when Kelsey turned and signaled, crossing his arms above his head in the universal sign of distress. But the driver passed by and went a couple hundred feet down the road before red brake lights appeared.

"California or bust!" Kelsey cheered as he slapped Jack on the back, and they sprinted toward the first ride on what they envisioned as their adventure of a lifetime. The driver took them to Grand Island, and where the highway crossed the Union Pacific mainline, the boys got out.

"Know anything about hopping a freight?"

"Not really. Suppose you just jump on and ride," Kelsey replied. "How hard can it be?"

"What if it's moving?"

"It will be. Heard tell the railroad bulls can be awful mean. If they catch you, they'll beat you and toss you off the train even if it's going 40 miles an hour. We can wait in the willows down along the river. When a train pulls out, we'll run out before it gets up a head of steam and hop on."

They hid in a thicket of scrub willows. Trash clung to the willow roots, exposed by the erosion of a flash flood. The sun arced into the open canopy of blue sky where a single puffy cloud hung passively, seemingly without ill intent. The day began to warm. A squat steam engine pushed cars along the tracks. A switchman threw switches, metal slammed into metal and couplers latched. As cars were being arranged in line, the boys kept a wary eye peeled toward the road, knowing any trouble would most likely come from that direction.

Jack played with reshaping his hat, denting it just so with the heel of his hand, pinching the crown and attempting to restore a slight roll to the flaccid brim. Off to one side, through a narrow gap in the willows, an adventuresome rabbit left the safety of the underbrush and was grazing on the succulent tops of newly emerging grass shoots.

"There's a rabbit over there," Jack whispered, and Kelsey was beginning to turn his head, when there was a blurring flash of wings, followed almost simultaneously by a shocking thud. A golden eagle had impaled the rabbit with its talons.

Now the eagle lifted in a graceful upward sweep. The rabbit hung below, shrieking in pain and fear.

"You see that?"

"I seen it."

A while later a sheriff's car, white star painted on the door, drove slowly along the road. Even though it was unnecessary, they ducked low until the car disappeared around a bend. A long train, never slowing, passed going east. An hour later, a steam locomotive, pushing before it noise and vibrations, approached from out of the east.

"This is it," Kelsey said, "Our passport to the coast. Wouldn't it be somethin' if she's high-ballin' straight through to California?"

The train—whistle wailing, bell clanging, metal screeching—came into view. The locomotive lumbered forward and the ground shook with its raw power. White steam pumped into still air like urgent breaths on a winter morning. The engineer released the brake and slowly pushed the throttle forward. The cacophony changed. Cars snapped at their couplings and energy passed through them like links in a chain, each growing a little louder, more potent, violent, until at last all the pent up force passed through the caboose and disappeared harmlessly into thin air at the back of the train.

"She ain't gonna stop!" Kelsey barked. He was already on his feet, running. He reached the first set of tracks, leaped both rails at once and ran alongside the train. But the train was moving almost faster than he could run. He took a quick peek over his shoulder, saw a ladder coming and reached for it. All in one fluid motion he gripped the metal and allowed the forward momentum of the train to swing him off his feet. He climbed up and propelled himself onto the car like a seasoned hobo.

Kelsey shouted encouragement to Jack. "Faster! Faster!"

Panic and determination were written on Jack's face as his stubby legs drove up and down like pistons. Wind pushed at the brim of his hat, causing it to flatten against the crown.

"Toss it up."

Jack pitched his duffel onto the bed of the car. But the effort knocked off his hat. It disappeared under the hard charging train. He made a desperate stab for the ladder, fingers blindly groped, curled around the thin, round bar and he was yanked off his feet. Using his well-developed upper body, he hoisted himself up the ladder and onto the surface of the rail car where his breath came in jagged gulps and his heart boomed against his ribcage.

"We did it!" The hard lines etched on Kelsey's face softened and he broke into a wide grin. "Son of a bitch! For a minute there I thought you were gonna blow a gasket. Your legs was pumpin' a mile a minute."

Jack lay flat on his back and was still trying to steady his racing heart and catch his breath. Later, sitting side-by-side with legs tucked up in front of them, they watched the countryside flash past and talked about how they were going to set the world on fire. Iron wheels passed over gaps between rails and made *clickity-clack, clickity-clack, clickity-clack* sounds as regular as the ticking of a grandfather clock marking seconds. The dirty plume from the engine's smokestack rolled back, clogging the blue sky, and the wind flowed and swirled. They could see and taste the sharp bite of smoke and feel grit on their tongues. Smoke stung their eyes while sun and wind burned their faces and necks. Telegraph wires curved between poles, wires dipping and lifting again and again like the swift and repetitive arc of a swallow's flight.

The skin on Jack's face felt hot, as though it had been stretched tight. There was a briny taste in his mouth and he tried to swallow, but did not have enough saliva. An endless procession of farmhouses, barns and fields—all sliding backwards—drifted past. He reassured himself that each mile they traversed was a buffer against the bad, while at the same time shortening the distance to a better future.

The rails began to follow the languid Platte River, its shoreline interspersed with willows and cottonwoods. Occasionally the tracks burst onto open fields that shone emerald green with growing corn, grain and grasses. Brown cows dotted pastures. Two calves soundlessly kicked up their heels and ran from the noisy train. Jack saw a dead cow, a pitiful thing with four feet pointed skyward and a bloated stomach about to burst with the swelling gas of putrefaction. A farmer guided a double-bottom plow pulled by a team of draft horses, sweat and white froth discoloring their sides. A black dog chased along behind the plow, intently watching for mice, and when a mouse was revealed the dog killed it quickly and tossed the lifeless body into the air for sport. A covey of quail flushed from brush along the tracks, matched the speed of the train and veered away. Three crows landed in a dead tree and another passed overhead, traveling south.

Jack caught a quick glimpse of a sod house, and then the image was gone. What remained were impressions of sod squares, deeply weathered trusses, pale moss, a manure pile where cows had stood in the lee to get out of the wind, and the withered clematis that the homesteader's wife had planted and nurtured with rinse water. In the far corner of a fenced-in area was a small white headstone marking a child's grave. Jack took a long, deep breath and lay back on the flat, rough boards. Vibrations massaged his muscles, eyelids fluttered, and as sleep robbed him of his senses, he knew he was freer, wilder and braver than he ever could have imagined.

He slept until the train slowed and pulled onto a siding in Julesburg, a tiny hamlet straddling the border between

Nebraska and Colorado. Hoping to rustle something to eat, they got off the train and walked into town. From the direction they were coming, and their sunburned and sooty faces, it was obvious to the policeman who spotted them, these boys were most likely runaways. He stepped from an alley and onto the boardwalk, intercepting them and motioning with his right hand that he wanted them to come to him.

"What's up, officer?" Kelsey asked.

"At first glance I thought you two was niggers," the policeman said with a laugh. And when the two boys seemed confused, he pointed toward a store window. They turned, and in the window's reflection saw their faces had been blackened by a harsh combination of sun, wind, coal dust and smoke. But Kelsey also noticed a poster taped to the window advertising an upcoming sporting event, a boxing smoker. It called for fighters and offered a $5 prize as an inducement to the winner of three weight classes: heavyweight, middleweight and lightweight.

"What you doing in town?"

Kelsey took a step and tapped the window with a knuckle. "Here for the smoker."

"Then you're a day late. That was last night. You missed a humdinger. You both fight?"

"Mostly just him." Kelsey motioned toward Jack. "I can fight, don't get me wrong, but he's good, real good."

"What's the name?"

Jack did not want to give his real name for fear the sheriff in Hastings had sent a wire up and down the line for all law enforcement officials to "be on the lookout for a fourteen-year-old runaway by the name of Jack Small." He blurted the first thing that came to his mind. "Nevada Kid, that's the name I fight under."

"Don't believe I've ever heard of you, and I follow the boxing game pretty close."

"Fight out of Reno," Jack lied.

Kelsey picked up on the diversion. "We're in the middle of a swing, went up to Idaho, into Wyoming, points east. We're on our way home."

"Reno, that home?"

"Yeah, but we move around a lot," Kelsey said. "Have to in the fight game."

"Tell you what, there's another smoker tonight down the line in Sedgwick. I'm going. Be glad to give you two a lift."

"Mighty nice of you," Kelsey allowed. The sounds of the westbound train departing became audible; the engine laboring to pick up speed, forlorn whistle blowing loud and long.

"You might want to clean up. There's a water trough in back of the livery—over there." The policeman gave a nod toward a building with a wooden false front. "When you finish, come by my office. It's down the street, right-hand side, you can't miss it."

The water in the trough was warm from standing in the sun all day. Jack stripped off his shirt and stuck his head under the water. He looked like a duck bobbing up and down. He scrubbed his face, making tight circles until his sunburned skin stung, and then he washed his arms and chest the same way.

Kelsey noticed a white envelope, folded and safety-pinned to the inside of the shirt Jack had thrown over the hitching rail.

Jack came up sputtering. "Feels mighty fine. Better give it a go, get some of the soot off."

Kelsey fingered the envelope. "What's gives with this? You ain't holding out on me, are you?"

"Hell no. Just a picture of Mom. Carry it around for good luck."

After bathing, the boys talked it over, and although they felt wary riding to the neighboring town with a policeman, they concluded if he had had any suspicions they were runaways they would already be under arrest. The overriding factor affecting their decision was they both figured Jack could easily win his fight and they desperately needed spending money for the road.

Jack signed up for the smoker in Sedgwick under the name Nevada Kid. They measured and weighed him—5' 5" and 122 pounds. He was entered in the lightweight division. When his opponent was introduced, a 21-year-old stonemason, the young man stripped off his robe, flexed his muscles and bounced around the ring like a peacock fanning his feathers for the benefit of a flock of hens. He danced near Jack and scoffed, "You ain't nothin' but a snot-nosed punk kid. I'll eat you alive."

At the opening bell, Jack met his adversary in the middle of the ring. They touched gloves in an obligatory show of sportsmanship. Jack faked as though he was taking a relaxed step backward, but instead moved forward, aggressively firing a straight right. The meat of his glove landed against his opponent's face. Nose cartilage cracked, blood spurted and all the bluster and bluff vanished as the stonemason collapsed onto the canvas, where he sat looking up at Jack. The fight referee raised the right arm of the Nevada Kid.

On the way to Sedgwick, the policeman had educated Jack, saying, "No prize money is paid. You make whatever the crowd thinks you're worth. They throw money into the ring. Go after the tips. Your opponent will be doing the same. You gotta be fast. Scoop up everything you can. You might win the fight, but still lose if you can't scramble."

Coins were being tossed onto the canvas and Jack used his knees to pry off a glove. With his free hand he scooped coins. Later, when he counted the money, he had $1.67. He told Kelsey, "Profit. Pure profit."

The two spent the night camped near Sedgwick. In the morning, to get on down the road, they turned to hitchhiking.

Jack fought again in the town of Brush, winning by a TKO. He won another in Stoneham. After that fight, they caught a ride to the mainline and hopped a freight train to Glenwood Springs so Jack could fight in a smoker being advertised for Friday night. They never made it. Coming into Denver, a pair of railroad dicks saw the boys drop off and with pistols drawn, arrested them for trespassing. They were hauled off to jail in a paddy wagon.

For the first several hours of his imprisonment, Jack paced back and forth like a caged animal until his cellmate, a petty thief who was going by the alias, Mason Jeffery, counseled, "Son, you gotta take time to do time. Don't be in a rush. Relax. Let time come to you. Time runs its own pace, its own race."

Mason peeled off his shirt to display an upper torso nearly covered with tattoos. "Here's what I do to pass time. I'm an artist. Did most everything myself, wherever I could reach." He was a walking billboard: a snarling tiger, a howling coyote, a variety of flowery designs, several drawings depicting the figures of nude women, the words "Brenda Forever" and "Love Iona," a kicking mule, a skull and crossbones, a knife dripping blood and several hearts, one of which was broken.

"I'll give you a tattoo," he offered. "No charge. Just to help pass the time."

"Naw. I wouldn't know what to put."

Mason flashed a grin and rolled his left shoulder. "How about a naked gal? Watch her dance." He flexed and the outline of an unclothed woman wiggled and squirmed over his undulating muscles.

"Don't think so."

But the seed of an idea had been planted and by the afternoon of Jack's second day of confinement, he was stretched across his bunk and Mason was busy working on a tattoo across Jack's stomach. Using blue ink and the sharp point of a safety pin, Mason was creating the words NEVADA, with the N and the A elongated, and tucked between the oversized letters was the word KID. The process was more painful and bloody than Jack ever dreamed it would be. The constant stabbing of the needle was unreasonably irritating and as the jailhouse artist worked to create his latest masterpiece, Jack fought the compulsive urge to scratch his stomach.

The following day, the duty sergeant stopped in front of their cell and bellowed down the corridor to the jailer, "What the hell's this kid still doing here? I said to get rid of him. I ain't running no boarding house."

He turned to Jack and lowered his voice. "You don't have no business being on the bum. Go back home where you belong."

"Can't."

"Why not?"

"Old man damn near beat me to death."

"Maybe so, but I'll tell you straight, the road ain't no place for a kid."

With a jangle of keys, the jailer opened the door. Jack stepped through. The door slammed shut with firmness and certainty behind him.

Mason called, "See you down the line."

"Maybe so." Jack lightly fingered his tender stomach. "Thanks. I guess."

On the way to the outside, Jack asked the jailer, "I came in here with a buddy. Know what happened to him?"

"Released."

"When"

"Last night."

"Wonder where he'd have gone?"

"Probably hanging around the beanery waiting for you to show your face. When you find him, the two of you best clear out. Them railroad dicks got your number. Be looking for you.

This time, they're apt to lay open your head and leave you 'side the tracks. My advice, take a bus to Salt Lake. Tell 'em you're Mormon. They take care of their own, those Mormons do."

Jack walked to the hobo jungle where a number of low-burning campfires winked among a grove of cottonwood trees. He found Kelsey sitting on his haunches at one of the fires, drinking weak coffee from a tin can while phantoms of orange and black played across his face in response to flames flaring and shrinking.

"You got yourself out early."

Kelsey looked up and grinned. "Good behavior."

They swapped stories about their time in jail. Jack pulled up his shirt and revealed his tattoo. It was beginning to scab over.

"Why'd you go do that?"

"Beat doin' nothing."

A westbound train approached and Jack and Kelsey wasted little time hopping it. The train sided in Granby, and fearing the railroad dicks would make a sweep of the train, the boys got off and hiked into town where they found a smoker was scheduled for the following day. They decided to spend the night and camped at the edge of a grain field.

Jack easily won his two preliminary matches. In the title fight, which was to pay $5 to the winner, his opponent was "Stone Hands" Hugh. It was claimed he was the amateur lightweight champion of Utah. Jack won on a decision, but it was a difficult fight. After the bout, fight promoter Tex Armstrong visited Jack in the dressing room. He said, "If you agree to a rematch in Salt Lake City, I'll put up $25, winner take all."

"For 25 bucks I'd fight Dempsey, one hand tied behind my back."

Tex produced a contract. Jack signed it. A photographer snapped a publicity photo of Jack, gloved hands held up in a classic boxing pose, to help promote the fight scheduled for the following Saturday at the Salt Lake City Armory.

✠✠✠✠✠✠

Jack and Kelsey rode a freight train to Ogden and hitchhiked to Salt Lake City, taking a room in a cheap hotel. Jack got a good night's sleep in a comfortable bed. On the day of the fight, he and Kelsey toured the Mormon Tabernacle. The grand organ was being played and Jack was astounded at the way sound engulfed the huge chamber. He stayed and listened until Kelsey said, "Buddy, we've got a big fight coming up and you need to get off your feet."

They returned to their room. Jack spent an hour resting and concentrating on Hugh's fighting style. He was a rather unorthodox fighter who bobbed and weaved and kept moving forward with unrelenting single-mindedness. Jack knew what he must do. He envisioned stepping to one side, sliding, jabbing and hooking. He played it over and over in his mind until it became a mantra—step, slide, jab, hook.

Salt Lake City was Hugh's hometown. It would be difficult for any fighter to come in and get a favorable decision. Jack knew that, knew his only chance would be to win by a TKO, and if he did he would be twenty-five bucks richer and they would have plenty of traveling money. Once they reached California, they would become movie stunt men.

The first two rounds of the fight could have gone either way. In the third, Hugh unleashed a two-punch combination sending Jack to the canvas, but he was back on his feet by the count of five and the bell saved him. At the start of the fourth round the referee stepped in front of Jack and asked, "Where are we?"

"Fighting." Jack's eyes were still glassy.

"What state are we in?"

91

"Salt Lake."

Those answers satisfied the referee. He stepped out of the way and motioned the fighters to fight. Hugh, sensing his opponent's vulnerability, rushed forward throwing punches. Jack could do nothing but cover up and retreat. He staggered backward until he came in contact with the ropes. He hung there with the ropes across his back, dimly aware of the slick taste of blood, the brush of wind from a blow that just missed his head and the rank odor of his sweat. He remembered that time with his dad, the way the black fighter leaned against the ropes, collapsed, bounced, and the way red oozed from his mouth. He refused to be knocked senseless like that. Digging deep he discovered a reservoir of strength he did not know he possessed. He used it to push Hugh away. He flicked a short left to his opponent's exposed ribs, while at the same time he brought around a thundering roundhouse right that caught Hugh on the side of his cheek and jaw. The bell sounded ending the round.

Jack went directly to his corner and sat on the stool. Kelsey flicked cold water in his face and said, "You got him on the run. You're doin' great. Stay aggressive!"

In rounds five and six, Jack was clearly the superior fighter. He put Hugh down for an eight count in the sixth, but he was a tough guy and refused to stay down. At the end of the fight, when the judges' cards had been tallied, Hugh was awarded the fight on a split decision. The crowd gave a robust cheer for their hometown champion.

In the dressing room, Tex slipped Jack a five spot and breathlessly said, "That was one hell of a fight! Son, you was robbed. We gotta have a rubber match. We'll do it at a neutral site. How about Los Angeles?"

"Suits me. We're headed in that direction anyway."

"I wanna tell you something," the fight promoter said. "Over the years I've seen fighters come and go. You've got as much, or more potential, than any of 'em. If you stay in the game, train hard and keep your nose clean, there's no reason in hell you can't become a world champion. And when you do, I want to be training and promoting you."

He handed Jack his business card. "When you get to L. A. give a call. I'll have a contract ready for you to sign. You'll be on my payroll."

Jack realized he might have lost the fight, but he had won the opportunity to become a professional fighter. And although he had one eye swollen and a jaw that hurt to open and close, and cuts in his mouth that continued to bleed, he was in high spirits. They hitchhiked back to Ogden, walked to the railroad yards and caught the ill-fated westbound freight.

Chapter Eight

When Jack had the opportunity to drop off the freight train in Nebraska like he had planned to do, he changed his mind and chose to continue on, riding all the way to Chicago. He disembarked on the south side and wandered uptown.

The destructive effects of the stock market crash, and the resulting Great Depression were everywhere: long lines of unemployed men waiting for relief food, or waiting for their turn at a soup kitchen, or standing in groups idly warming their hands over garbage can fires. Jack was cold to the bone, hungry, and tired. His stump was rubbed raw from chaffing on the prosthesis, and the straps had worn sores on his hip and thigh. He limped along seeking a warm, quiet place where he could catch a few hours sleep.

On Halsted Street he came to the stage entrance of the *Star and Garter Theater* where dancer Gypsy Rose Lee was billed on the marquee as the featured attraction. Opposite the theater was a brick wall surrounding a brownstone building. On the far end of the wall was an iron gate. Jack, for the hell of it, tried the handle. It opened. He stepped through. A vent was sending a cloud of steam into the cold night air. Jack huddled there and before long the warmth made him drowsy. He slumped against the wall and fell asleep.

A burly man with a boxer's flattened nose yanked Jack to his feet and held him in a vice-like grip. A tall man, dressed nattily—wearing a gray overcoat over a dark blue, double-breasted suit, white cotton shirt, striped tie, a snap brim hat and holding a rattan cane—looked Jack over. The dandy barked, "You breakin' in? Is that what you was doin'?"

"No," Jack protested.

The pug twisted Jack's arm and growled, "Shut the hell up."

"So you was gonna steal from me," the dandy continued. "A little punk like you thinks he can sneak in...."

A woman spoke. "Damn it, Johnny. You can see he's just a kid. All he's doing is looking to get warm. He fell asleep."

The woman stepped from the shadows into view. She had stunning good looks, and even though the evening was cold, she was wearing a simple wrap over a sleeveless straight-line sheath dress, lilac-colored with several shades of mauve sequins sewn onto the expensive material. She wore silk stockings, her shoes had Louis heels, and her black hair was bobbed and shingled. She took hold of the dandy's arm.

"That right?" the man asked.

Jack nodded.

"Don't believe 'im," the pug groused.

"Let him go, Max," the woman directed. Then she turned to Johnny and pleaded, "I got a brother his age. He didn't mean no harm. Can't you see he's shivering?"

When sympathy failed, the woman tried a different approach. "Johnny, you never started out on top. Remember what it was like? Come on, give the kid a break."

Johnny pointed the end of his fancy cane at Jack. "Okay." He gave a slight nod and the big man loosened his grip. Jack was free. He rubbed his right arm.

"Where you from?" Johnny asked.

"Nebraska. But I'm coming from Nevada. That's where I've been; was in Nevada."

"What you doin' in my town?"

"I want to get a job. Look for one anyway." Jack tried to run his hand through his hair. It was wet and stiff from the cold. The hair stood on end.

"Ain't gonna be easy. Jobs are few and far between. What's your name?"

Jack told him.

The dandy said, "That's Max. He's my bodyguard, and this here's Libby. Keep your mitts off her, she's mine." He was grinning at the very thought something might develop between this scruffy kid and his gorgeous moll. "And I'm Johnny O'Donnell. Maybe you've heard of me."

Jack bobbed his head up and down as if to acknowledge he had actually heard of the small-time hoodlum.

"What you hear?" Johnny wanted to know.

"Hear 'bout what?"

"Me. What you hear 'bout me?"

Jack thought fast. "Heard you was a stand-up guy. Could be trusted; man of his word."

"See, told you he was alright," Libby said. "No sense standing out here in the cold trading pleasantries. I'm freezing. Johnny, why don't you invite our new friend inside?"

"Ah, sure," Johnny said, "come on in. Hey, you must be starved. Max, run up to the corner and get a sandwich—make it a steak sandwich—for the kid."

The interior of the brownstone was lavishly decorated around an exceedingly well-stocked bar. Johnny went directly to the bar, poured two drinks, gave one to Libby and sipped from the second. He asked Jack, "Want a Coca-Cola?"

"Sure."

Johnny opened a bottle, held it out. Jack limped across the room to get it. "Thanks," he said.

"I've gotta make a call."

As soon as Johnny was gone into the next room, Libby said, "I don't mean to be nosey, but I see the way you walk. Got a bum leg?"

"Yeah."

"Polio?"

Jack shook his head.

She dropped the subject. "You been traveling?"

Jack was embarrassed that the conversation was centered on him. He wanted to turn the tables and thank the young lady for saving him from a beating, but felt unsure of himself in her presence. She was so pretty and was wearing such nice clothes. Jack glanced at his dirty shirt and trousers and was even more uncomfortable.

Libby lit a cigarette and took a contemplative puff. "So tell me how do you earn traveling money?"

Jack hunched his shoulders. "I was doing a little boxing, going around picking up fights at smokers. Before my accident."

She cautiously asked, "Want to talk about it?"

"No. Not really."

Jack was hiding something, but that was okay because Libby was hiding something, too. She was Johnny's girl, expected to be a part of the scenery and nothing more—simply a pretty little vase of fresh-cut flowers, nice to look at, but with hardly any lasting substance—and she knew that, like that bouquet, her beauty would soon fade and she would be tossed aside. She recently had noticed dimples on the fleshy part of her legs and small lines were starting to show around her eyes, although for the time being she could hide those with makeup. Just last week she plucked a few white hairs from her scalp. She accepted, and yet despised the obvious truths of aging. She wondered what her family would think if they knew how she was living. How much longer would Johnny, or someone like Johnny, want her?

Libby pounded her cigarette into a glass ashtray, finished her drink in one long pull and stated, "Nice to meet you, Jack Small. I'm going to turn in. Good night."

"Good night. And say, thanks for what you did for me."

"You're welcome."

Jack watched as Libby departed the room—the way she placed her steps in a flawless line and swung her hips—and he could not begin to speculate how long it had taken her to perfect such a seductive gait. He sat listening to the sounds of her heels tapping the hardwood floors, climbing the stairs, and ending when she kicked off her shoes at the entrance to the bedroom. He thought of her undressing, pulling the dress over her head, rolling down her silk stockings.

There were heavy footsteps and Max, huffing and puffing, made his way into the room and tossed a paper sack in Jack's direction. "Here's your goddamned sandwich."

He proceeded to the bar where he fixed himself a stiff drink. Jack was efficiently devouring the steak sandwich when Johnny re-entered the room. Max spoke to him, "Want me to kick the kid out?"

"Don't guess so," Johnny replied. He glanced in Jack's direction. "For some odd reason Libby's taken a likin' to him. He stays. Jack, tell you what I'm gonna do. You bunk in that room over there, but for Christ's sake clean yourself up before you crawl between the sheets. We'll talk in the morning. Maybe I can find something for you to do around here."

With that said, Johnny went upstairs to join Libby. Jack went to his designated room, stripped off his clothes, sat in a chair and unfastened his prosthesis. He tried to rub a little circulation into his stump and winced at the pain. He hopped into the bathroom, drew a tub of water and washed. When he went to bed, he pulled the covers over him and was asleep as soon as his head hit the pillow.

When he awoke, Max was standing over him, saying, "You lucky son of a bitch. Johnny's gonna keep ya around and put ya ta work." He tossed onto the bed a stack of clothes—trousers, shirts, socks, underwear and even a pair of shoes—along with the admonishment, "Put these on."

Jack soon learned that Johnny O'Donnell was a small-time mobster dealing in a number of unlawful activities, but primarily running illegal whiskey he imported from Canada. He sold two brands, White Mule and Brown Mule. The difference between the two? White Mule was cut with water and Brown Mule with prune juice. Brown Mule was twice as expensive as White Mule. Jack's first job was in a warehouse making the cut, filling half-pint and pint bottles. He worked diligently and never complained about the long hours or how much the standing hurt his bad leg.

Johnny and Libby attended parties on an almost nightly basis, sometimes asking Jack if he wanted to tag along. When he did, he usually found a remote corner where he could hide away and observe the goings on. He watched Johnny, Libby dangling loosely on his arm, work the room, leaving every person he came in contact with smiling in his wake.

It was at one of these parties that Jack was introduced to Harley Day, a cat burglar who specialized in night robberies. The tools of his trade were ropes, guile and guts. He operated out of an upscale flat on Roosevelt Boulevard, sleeping away the day and waiting for dark of night to ply his trade.

In advance of their meeting, Johnny had talked to Harley, telling him, "Jack works for me; does a little of this, little of that. Says he was a boxer, but got himself hurt, lost a leg, but handles himself pretty goddamn good for a cripple.

"He's a country kid, honest as the day is long. For the past couple weeks he's been bunking at my place, but I think it's time he found a new spot to hang his hat. Harley, I'd consider it a personal favor if you was to put him up."

"Sure thing, Johnny," Harley promised.

As soon as Johnny made the introductions he moved away. After a little small talk Harley got around to suggesting Jack move in with him, saying, "I got a two bedroom walk-up and if you was to move in, it'd help me out with the rent. I want someone there when I'm not. I don't need some asshole sneaking around and stealing me blind."

Jack moved in with Harley, and he continued to work for Johnny, bottling and delivering alcohol, occasionally running numbers, sometimes picking up protection payoffs from merchants. He enjoyed all the benefits of his lifestyle: a nice place to live, plenty to eat, entertaining parties to attend and real spending money in his pocket. He became well-schooled in the underworld and the nuances of surviving by criminal guile. Jack thought life was good, so good he hardly took notice as Indian summer held into late October, and the rising and setting sun shone blood red behind the autumn veil of pollution and air-borne dust. Migratory birds amassed their squadrons and practiced maneuvers over the city in preparation for flying south. Doves, mostly unseen during the long summer, emerged from hiding places and sat in tight clusters on telephone and electric lines cooing to each other.

The weather changed abruptly. The hazy blue sky took on a menacing quality, becoming a low canopy of gray muslin. It was no longer warm during the day. The once green leaves, already having ruptured into orange and yellow, sprang to life. They turned and twisted before an insolent north wind that slapped the leaves free, sending them zigzagging downward to scurry across sidewalks and bank against fences, buildings, and any other slight obstruction.

Far to the south, in the Gulf of Mexico, a swirling mass of moist warm air hooked north, following the Mississippi River, and met with an arctic front sliding down over Illinois. Rains came. Leaves gathered in gutters, plugged drains, and water stood in graceless puddles at every intersection. Birds departed in haste. Rain turned to snow, and before the big storm retreated, a foot of fresh white had fallen over the cityscape, signaling the start of yet another raw Chicago winter.

Jack, lost in his work and immersed in the pleasures of self-indulgence, gave only passing notice to the fickleness of Mother Nature. In addition to the change in weather, he failed to comprehend the obvious magnitude of the Great Depression. The streets of Chicago had become camps for the unfortunate who could not find work. They gathered together in unhappy groups, ate scraps of food gleaned from trash cans, and drank weak coffee from cups and tin cans. As evenings descended, the army of heartbroken men clung to their faded photographs of family: daughters or sisters with cute curls and colorful ribbons, sons or brothers with hair slicked back and work shirts tucked into trousers, mothers, fathers, wives, girlfriends. The photographs they carried had been rained on, creased and folded. When enough time elapsed the treasured photographs would dissolve into nothingness. These destitute disciples of a failed federal economy were simply trying to make it through another long, stormy Chicago night. If they did survive, maybe in the morning they would head south, just as the great flocks of migratory birds had been doing for thousands of years.

Jack attended yet another party, and here he met mobster, John Dillinger. They drank bootleg whiskey, talked for the better part of an hour, and all the while Dillinger's wide-set eyes darted nervously around the room, as if he was expecting trouble but was not sure from which direction it might come. When Dillinger was ready to move away he told Jack, "Kid, I like your style. Down the line I might come up with something for you. I'll let you know."

Jack had begun to idolize men like Dillinger; men who operated according to their own set of right and wrong and were bigger than life. He was excited at the possibility of working for the most notorious of all Chicago's gangsters. In his estimation, just living in the shadow of such social outlaws made his life full of risk, danger and excitement. He liked that.

After months of winter the snow and cold eventually gave way to springtime and warmer weather. One glorious day in May, Jack was strolling along a deserted sidewalk, enjoying the sun on his face, when an automobile suddenly shot from an alley, careened dangerously across Olive Street and screeched to a stop a few scant inches from him. A uniformed police officer leaped from the passenger's side, opened the back door and forcefully shoved Jack onto the seat. He crawled in beside Jack and slammed the door shut as the cop behind the wheel popped the clutch. The car lurched forward and roared away down the street.

Jack assumed he was being arrested, but when nothing was said, he began to speculate these men might not be cops at all, but rival hoodlums. He was being taken for a ride, where at some desolate location they would shove him out the door and he would die in a hail of bullets. Jack looked around. The door handle was missing. There was no avenue of escape.

Approaching Calumet Park the car braked and skidded to a stop. The cop seated next to Jack growled, "We captured Harley Day; caught him red-handed. We could arrest you as an accomplice."

Jack started to protest, but the second cop turned in his seat and barked, "Shut the hell up!"

"We know you run numbers and sell bootleg whiskey for Johnny O'Donnell," the first cop said. "We could nail your ass ten ways from Sunday."

The driver said, "But we're gonna give you a break." He pointed through the windshield to a post with wooden arrows nailed to it noting the names of cities and towns and their distances away in miles. "Go to Indianapolis, Columbus, Detroit, Cincinnati. Go anywhere. But don't you ever come back to Chicago. If you do, swear to God, we'll send you up to the big house and it'll be umpteen years 'fore you ever see the light of day."

"Why you givin' me a break?"

"Figure you made a mistake in judgment, got in over your head. Let me tell you, this here ain't no kinda life for a crippled kid. Now get the hell out 'fore we change our minds."

Jack exited the automobile. The grim-faced driver made a quick U-turn and sped north, back to the heart of Chicago. Jack stared at Lake Michigan in the distance, so blue it looked as if the sky had turned upside down. He watched a squadron of ducks flash overhead, whistling the air with their wing tips. Then he buttoned his pea coat to protect himself against the raw wind that was blowing in off the lake, shoved his hands deep in his pockets and allowed his fingers to absently play with a few stray bills and an odd assortment of coins in his pockets. He guessed it best to keep that pesky wind at his back and start walking south.

The sound of an approaching truck caused Jack to turn and jab the air with his thumb. The truck passed and then the driver relented, responding slowly, letting off on the gas, braking, and pulling onto the shoulder of the road. Jack hobbled toward the truck. As he pulled himself up and onto the seat he asked, "Where you headed?"

"Oklahoma City," the driver said, "How 'bout you?"

Jack smiled. "Oklahoma City."

Upon reaching Oklahoma, Jack learned the entire Midwest was also suffering under the harsh effects of the Great Depression, as well as several years of drought. Farmers were giving up and moving away. Jobs were almost nonexistent.

He asked for work at the Oklahoma City Stockyard. The yardman responded, "Ain't got no work here, but ya might wanna check the depot. Sometimes they allow down-and-outers ta carry baggage fer people in exchange fer tips. Be worth a shot. Never know 'less ya ask."

He found the depot clerk, a nondescript man wearing tan trousers, starched white shirt and orange suspenders, in a foul mood. Jack asked, "Mind if I hang around and carry luggage for tips?"

"Beat it."

All Jack wanted to do was a little honest work in the hope he could scrape together enough to pay for a meal. Even though he had been denied the opportunity, he was reluctant to leave.

"I ain't tellin' ya again; get the hell out of here."

Jack walked along the boardwalk, hearing his footfalls sounding hollow and solitary. He was mad and he was hungry. Near the end of the landing a suitcase sat alone, unclaimed it seemed. On impulse, he picked it up and kept walking as nonchalantly as possible. He did not stop until he reached a grove of cottonwood trees a quarter-mile from the depot.

The case was made of leather, dyed black, but worn through in several spots to expose the natural brown of the cow. He tried to open the case, but the lock refused to yield and he was forced to beat the stubborn lock with a rock before it finally succumbed. The case held candy samples. There was an assortment of Baby Ruth, Bit-O-Honey, Black Cow and Charleston Chews.

Jack knew it belonged to a traveling salesman, some fellow poor as a church mouse who probably had a family waiting for him at home. He had stolen from a workingman and he felt bad. His first impulse was to return the suitcase, but he quickly rejected that idea as too risky. Instead he stuffed his pockets with candy, discarded the case and walked to the highway where he stood on the shoulder of the road and jabbed with his thumb, anxiously imploring any driver headed west to pick him up.

He was ignored until a dilapidated truck hauling empty wooden crates braked and pulled over onto the shoulder. As he hurried to catch the ride the thought crossed his mind: it was always the people with the least who were the first to come to the aid of their fellow man.

When his ride turned south, Jack was let out in the tiny hamlet of McLean, Texas. He walked under the tall spraddle legs of the town's water tower, passed several buildings crowded together behind false fronts, glanced in the direction of the bank and then the post office beneath a giant American flag rippling in the wind. He ate his last Baby Ruth candy bar standing in front of the McLean Market. The sugary sweetness of the chocolate only seemed to stimulate his gnawing desire for real food.

The town, from all outward appearances, was deserted. And then, from somewhere out of sight, cheering became audible and Jack knew there was a baseball game in progress and everyone in town was there.

He looked up and down the empty street and slipped to the back of the market where he pried open a window and squirmed through the narrow opening. Harley had said burglary was easy, but no matter how many times you commit the crime, the excitement was always there. What fed Jack's tension was not knowing if the coast was clear or if he would be met by a man with a shotgun.

The store was deserted and he stole a thick-cut steak from the meat case, a can of pork and beans, four sardine tins, a loaf of bread and a pair of apples from a bushel bin. He stepped to the cash register, hit "no-sale" and rifled the cash drawer, taking only a single $5 bill and a small handful of nickels, dimes and quarters.

On the way out of town, he gave the ball field a wide berth and hiked cross-country. As the sun began to set, shadows, long and distorted, played over the barren countryside. Darkness triumphed and he returned to the highway where the walking was easier. Each time lights signaled an approaching vehicle, he stepped off the road and hid in the bushes until it passed. A quarter-moon rose, bringing a soft illumination to the night. He walked under that moon until finally stopping in a secluded dry wash, starting a small fire with mesquite as fuel. He kept it burning low as he cooked the steak skewered on a stick. The meat dripped fatty juices into the red coals and sparkling shafts of blue and red flames flickered in the night. Off to the edge of the fire, the can of pork and beans made *blurp-blurp-blurping* noises. He used his pocketknife as an all-purpose utensil, devouring the meal quickly. When finished, he wiped the blade on his pant leg, kicked out the fire and returned to the highway.

The food satisfied his appetite, but left him with an ache in his heart. It was one thing to collect a debt for Johnny O'Donnell, even protection money, and it was quite another to steal to satisfy his personal needs. He justified his recent theft by telling himself he could have cleaned out the cash drawer. He figured the grocer would probably never even suspect he had been robbed. Jack kept walking until at long last dawn puffed ghost gray. The sky was glowing yellow and the sun was threatening to emerge over a distant hill when he finally caught a ride with a farmer taking a load of pigs to market.

In Amarillo, he earned a day's wages helping an old man repair a picket fence damaged by a runaway truck. He used the buck he was paid to buy food and the $5 he had stolen in McLean to buy a new pair of boots and a change of clothes. And then he was back on the road, hitchhiking west; always west toward California. Along the way he stopped for a day, a few days, or even a week or two when he found a paying job: hauling hay, sorting potatoes, building fence, painting a barn, piling rocks, driving tractor, cleaning plows, greasing discs, pulling tumbleweeds from under barbed wire fences and feeding cattle. The jobs never amounted to much. Sometimes his only pay was a meal, or the hayloft of a barn where he bunked for the night.

Dear Mother,

Thought I'd drop you a line, let you know I've been working in the hay harvest for a rancher near a one-horse town called Standing Rock. It's in New Mexico, a ways west from the Continental Divide. A lot of Zuni Indians live around these parts. They don't have much to say. The country is real pretty with high red rock mesas and plenty of tall grass wherever there is water.

I've gotten used to my leg. It don't hardly bother me at all no more. I can do whatever the next man can.

I've got it in my mind to see California. Maybe I'll run out there and then double back for a visit. A lot of time has gone by since I saw all of you last. I think about you often. I'll just bet Nellie and Donny are so growed up I'd have a hard time recognizing them. I'll write again real soon.

Love,

Jack

As he mailed his letter, he was certain of two things: he loved his mother and yet he would never be able to forgive her. If she had interceded on his behalf and stopped the beatings, he never would have run away and his body would still be whole.

The trouble with his stepfather began not long after he returned from the orphanage. Grace had grudgingly admitted to her husband that Jack misbehaved and that was the reason he was expelled.

One morning at the breakfast table Chet announced, "I think Jack should come with me. If he pays attention he just might learn something. Besides, folks are likely to be more generous if they know I'm a family man."

On the drive into downtown Denver, he explained what he expected of Jack. "When I get the crowd primed, I'll give you a nod and introduce you. I want you to step up, hold your hat in front of people and make them feel uncomfortable enough so they are compelled to donate to the cause. You do a good job and I'll buy you a dish of ice cream."

He parked his Ford and told Jack to hop out while he lingered behind the wheel, removed a small flask from the breast pocket of his coat and fortified himself with a shot of bootleg whiskey. He did not view alcohol as a crutch, but did recognize it gave him a certain advantage, sparking a fire of passion to his message. A second time he tipped the flask and then he screwed down the cap. He was ready.

At the corner of Federal Boulevard and Colfax Avenue, he placed his apple crate on the sidewalk, stood on top of it, cleared his throat and in a loud baritone voice began speaking.

"Ladies and gentlemen, please gather around. Are you despairing about the decay in our society? Do you detest the ever-eroding sanctity of family life, the degeneration of the fibers that hold us together as a nation? Then please listen to what I have to say."

After a lengthy speech regaling the extravagance and self-gratification of the current American culture and society, he concluded his remarks by saying, "You must stand up against the sins and the sinners. You must become an active participant. And now I ask you, I beseech you, to give to the cause of righteousness. Show your support against the decadence of the decade." Chet nodded to Jack. "My son Jack will pass the hat among you. Donate what you can. Please be generous. Without your support I cannot afford to bring my important messages to the masses. Thank you. Thank you so very much for your kindheartedness."

⊢⊣⊢⊣⊢⊣⊢

When Chet was a single man, street preaching provided him with enough easy spending money that it satisfied his personal needs. But now, even though he enlisted Jack to work the crowd and sometimes called on Grace and Nellie too, collections were never enough to sustain the family. Grace tried as best she could to stretch the money and make ends meet, but she felt it was like trying to push back the tide. She urged him to find a more stable income, a steady job.

One evening, Chet came rolling through the doorway with real excitement in his voice, calling out, "I've found a solution to our financial dilemma."

Grace was in the kitchen. "What is it this time?"

"Promise me you'll hear me out, not make any snap judgments; listen all the way through before you make up your mind. Promise?"

Grace continued to dice onions on the cutting board while casting an anxious glance in his direction, hoping he really did have an answer, but sincerely doubting it. She nodded for him to continue.

110

He spread the fingers on one hand and ran them comb-like straight back across his scalp. He knew better than almost anyone what it took to persuade a reluctant customer and close a deal. He opened his gambit by attempting to have her agree with him. "Would you concede this fact, that nearly everyone has a sweet tooth?"

Before she could agree or disagree, Nellie awoke from her nap and cried for attention. Grace went to her and returned to the kitchen carrying the child on her hip. He was waiting and pressed for an answer. "Well, do you agree?"

"I'd venture to say that *almost* everyone has a sweet tooth. What's that suppose to prove?"

"It proves the point that I've hit on something that will make us rich."

He removed a slip of paper from his pocket and jubilantly held it above his head.

"This is guaranteed to be the most tasty recipe known to mankind. No fooling."

"Recipe for what?"

He whispered each word. "Angel. Almond. Macaroons."

She was unable to restrain her laughter. Chet paid her no mind and his words plowed a straight furrow like a farmer following behind a mule. "Start small, right here at home. You're a hell of a cook. I've told you that at least a million times. You cook, I sell. We can't miss.

"Now, for the most exciting news of all. On the way home I swung by the market, gave Frank Gilbert a sample of Angel Almond Macaroons, and he was so taken that he placed an order, wants to start off with eight-dozen. Before long he'll double that, then double that again, and...."

"Once we hit the big time we'll buy a building, hire cooks, hire salesmen, have a fleet of delivery vans, sit back and rake in the profits. We'll have more money than you can shake a stick at.

"But don't let me talk you into something. Here, I have a sample. Taste for yourself. If this cookie does not tantalize your taste buds and enliven your senses, I'll take back the recipe, say I'm not interested and get my money back."

"How much did you spend?"

"Don't you worry your pretty little head about that." He removed a handkerchief from his coat pocket, carefully unwrapped the corners and revealed a portion of a single cookie. He broke off a small chunk and hand-fed it to her. Nellie whined for a taste and he obliged, breaking off a tiny piece and feeding it to her too. She responded enthusiastically by smacking her lips and crying for more.

"See, even baby thinks it's good."

"Oh, it's good. But how much did you pay?"

"Drop in the bucket. Nothing really."

"How much of a drop?"

"Five down, twenty when we clear our first hundred bucks. Not bad. Can't go wrong on a deal like that."

That evening Grace trudged to the market and charged the necessary ingredients to make a big batch of Angel Almond Macaroons. The following morning she rose early to warm the oven and begin mixing the ingredients. The cookies were cooling on racks when she went to wake Jack. His breakfast included his usual bowl of mush as well as one cookie to nibble on and another as a treat with his lunch. He ate the second cookie on the way to school, he liked the cookies that much.

Chet, who claimed he was not a morning person, finally rolled out of bed and wolfed down several Angel Almond Macaroons with his coffee. He never bothered tossing a single compliment in Grace's direction, but insisted, "Pack them a dozen to a bag. I'll have all these sold before you know it. And you better start on the next batch."

When school let out, Chet was waiting for Jack. The other kids went merrily on their way home, but Chet unloaded Jack's red wagon and packed it with bags of cookies. He instructed, "I want you to sell these on your way home—two bits a bag. Understand this—if you don't sell them, no dinner."

"Who's going to buy cookies?"

"Not my problem. Go door-to-door around the neighborhood."

"I don't know if I can do that."

"Sure you can. Get going." He gave Jack an open-handed pop on the seat of his trousers, got in his Ford and drove away, leaving Jack full of apprehension, insecurity and fear. But knowing he best not go home until he had sold every last bag of cookies, Jack crossed over two blocks to Hawthorne Street, passed the house on the corner because it did not look as if anyone was home, and pulled his wagon to a stop where a gray-haired woman was sweeping her porch. He screwed up his courage and called, "Lady, wanna buy some cookies?"

The woman, a grandmother several times over, beamed at the boy. "How much?"

"Two bits. You get a dozen."

"Are they any good?"

His face brightened. "Yes, ma'am. Real, real good. My mom made 'em."

"Oh she did, did she? In that case I do believe I'll take a dozen. Wait right here. I have to fetch my change purse."

Jack soon discovered not every sale was as easy as his first. The most common complaint from potential customers was that the cookies were overpriced, double the cost of sugar or peanut butter cookies from the bakery. But he was quick-witted. To overcome this negative he learned to stress the quality of his macaroons and even began offering new customers a small piece of cookie as a sample. Usually the rich taste did the trick and finalized the sale. Of course it was difficult for a boy not to nibble on a few of the samples.

Selling cookies became a routine. Every afternoon after school Chet was waiting with the red wagon loaded with cookies and he expected results. But one evening the weather was especially nasty, cold and rainy, and few customers were in the mood to buy cookies. Jack returned home with most of the cookies unsold and very little change to give his stepfather. Without saying anything, Chet stripped off his belt, grabbed Jack roughly by the shirt collar and delivered two hard swats across the back of his legs.

"I warned you what would happen if you didn't sell. Tomorrow you better sell or you'll get more of this." He made the leather belt pop. Off to the side Grace stood silently, watching but doing nothing in defense of her son.

The following evening Jack did not reach home until half-past seven. But his wagon was empty. He filled Chet's waiting hands with coins.

"Well, I guess you learned a valuable lesson last night."

And Jack had. He dreaded the belt more than he feared his customers' refusals. And in the course of this revelation he was forced to overcome a very humiliating experience. That situation occurred when he knocked on a door and a woman answered. She was in the shadows behind the screen door. He immediately launched into his practiced spiel, "Good day, ma'am. Perhaps you would be interested in purchasing a dozen of the most flavorful cookies you could ever hope to sink your teeth into, Angel Almond Macaroons. They are guaranteed fresh and…."

"Jack, is that you?" a familiar voice said.

With a rush of embarrassment, he realized the voice belonged to his teacher, Mrs. Mason.

"You sell cookies door-to-door?"

Jack simply nodded. That was all he could do.

"Is it to help earn money for your family?"

Again he nodded.

"How many are in a bag?" Mrs. Mason questioned.

"A dozen. I can give you a taste if you want."

"That won't be necessary. I believe I'd like to try a dozen."

The following day at school, Mrs. Mason addressed the class. "I know after school, and on weekends, most of you enjoy playing. But there is one person in this room doing something of much greater consequence. This individual is helping his family. He is...." She almost said the words "selling cookies" and was going to praise Jack by name when she glanced in his direction and saw him sliding down in his seat, his face turning an intense shade of red. She stopped and glanced away. "I want this particular individual to know how very proud I am of what he is doing."

As a cookie salesman, Jack suffered in a variety of ways. He was self-conscious that his family was poor and that it was necessary for him to work. He was smaller than almost all his classmates and was not handsome or cute or adorable as some of the other boys were said to be. And although Mrs. Mason's praise was embarrassing, it also made him feel slightly better because someone had acknowledged his contribution.

He might have told his mother about what had happened, but he never had the opportunity. When he arrived home Chet was in the kitchen, a place he rarely was seen except at mealtime. He was busy setting the table and dishing up the hot food. He even pulled out the chair, seated Grace and affectionately kissed the top of her head.

As soon as everyone finished eating, he gave a furtive glance in Grace's direction and with a great deal of pride, announced,

"Exciting news. We're going to have an addition to our family. You're going to have a baby brother or baby sister."

"Chet," Grace protested, "I thought we agreed I'd tell them."

"You tell them. I tell them. What the hell difference does it make?"

He shoved his chair away from the table, stomped to the coat rack, shrugged on his coat, tossed his hat on his head and declared, "I'll be back later."

When the baby boy was born, Chet insisted on naming him Donny, in honor of his favorite uncle. Donny was born with a mass of black hair, just like Chet's, and was blessed with his mother's brown eyes. For the most part the baby was easy to care for and fun-loving, but like any child he had moments when nothing seemed to please him. During those times, Chet displayed infinite patience for the child he liked to call *My Boy*. When Donny was teething, Chet dipped his finger in a glass of whiskey and rubbed his baby's gums. He bounced Donny on his knee and played with him. When he had difficulty sleeping, Chet rocked him. When he needed burping, Chet turned him over on his lap and gently patted his little back. But Chet drew the line at dirty diapers. When Donny was messy, Chet handed him to Grace.

Having a baby certainly added another layer of labor to Grace's busy schedule. No matter how long or how hard she worked there never seemed to be enough hours in the day to complete every task there was involved in being a full-time mother, wife, baker and businesswoman. Chet lost interest in cookies and by default Grace assumed the duties of operating all aspects of the business.

He drifted back into his old ways and refused to allow her to pin him down on where he went or what he was doing. He often came in late at night reeking of alcohol and stale cigarette smoke. If he had won at cards and was feeling flush, he might throw a few bucks on the table, but more often than not, she discovered money missing from her purse, or from the cookie jar where she kept loose change.

If she mentioned missing money, if she pushed him in any way, he stayed away from home to punish her. She wondered if he was involved with another woman and redoubled her efforts to make sure the house was spotless, the children well-behaved, appetizing food was on the table, and she was a willing partner in the bedroom.

One evening he came home unusually early, turned on the radio and sat in his favorite chair. Jack was on the floor, playing with Donny and tickling Nellie. Chet snapped, "Knock it off. I can't hear over your damn racket. Jack, go help your mother."

Apparently he did not respond fast enough. Chet kicked out with the pointed toe of his polished shoe, catching Jack in the pit of his stomach and causing him to lose his wind. He nearly fell on the baby, but was able to roll to the side. He came up on all fours and scrambled into the kitchen.

Grace noticed his red face and the way he took little gasps trying to fill his lungs. She asked, "What's the matter?"

"Nothing. What can I do to help?"

‡‡‡‡‡‡‡

The first Friday of every month was set aside to pay bills. This chore began only after the children had been put to bed and then Chet and Grace sat on opposite ends of the table with the bills scattered between them. He was the one who decided how to dole out various amounts of money to the grocer, the butcher, the iceman, the milk man....

If he had been drinking, any little thing could send him into a meanspirited tirade. On one first Friday of the month, he reacted to a particular receipt by banging his fist down and demanding to know, "What the hell did you buy here?" He shoved the offending paper in her direction.

She took a look. "Two yards of material. I made myself a dress. It was ninety-seven cents."

"I want you to know, I had a nice little nest egg salted away until you and those kids of yours came along. You've robbed the nest. There are no more eggs for you to steal. We're broke. Flat broke. And what do you do? Spend ninety-seven cents like it was nothing at all."

Even though tears welled in her eyes, she spoke thoughtfully and deliberately. "I bake every day, make deliveries and find new customers. When I'm out in public, I need to look presentable. I don't think one new dress a year is unreasonable. Look at what I'm wearing. It's threadbare. At least I'm working. Exactly what is it you do, Chet?"

He pushed himself away from the table with such force he knocked over his chair in the process. "I won't have you questioning, or criticizing me." The door slammed behind him and the house grew quiet, extremely quiet. Jack, having listened to the confrontation, lay in bed afraid to so much as draw a breath.

The following morning, Chet shook Jack awake. "Get a move on. You're coming with me today."

Jack, with sleep still clinging to his eyelids, found himself bouncing along in Chet's Ford down a rutted farm lane toward the eastern horizon that was now beginning to glow a pale rose color. All that long, hot, dry, dusty day he tried to keep up with his stepfather who moved proficiently down endless rows of towering cornstalks, snapping off corn ears with a quick twist of his wrist, chucking the ears into wooden crates. His forearms bulged; sweat rolled and all the while there was a steadiness to the cadence, like the beat of a bass drum, as ears of corn bounced off the side of the wooden crates.

Jack was much slower. That was to be expected, but he did not see it that way. By not being able to keep up, he felt as though he was letting down everyone in the family. If he had only pushed harder to sell the Angel Almond Macaroons, none of this would be necessary. He blamed himself for the family's financial predicament.

The farmer paid wages at the end of the day. He counted $2.19 into Chet's open hand and only 29 cents into Jack's hand. He gave his money to Chet.

Chapter Nine

As cancer consumed Florien, cell by unwilling cell, Red cared for the failing woman, trying to make her last days as comfortable as possible. She dabbed her patient's hot forehead with a cool washrag, brought water, and tucked a blanket around the withered shoulders when the chills took over and threatened to consume the last bit of life that remained in the ravished body.

She often sat beside the sick, silent woman, and invariably her thoughts reverted to Montana, back to when her mother was still alive. They had lived in the little shack owned by Ed Hall, where they had moved after Ed—with the help of attorney Ralph Thurman—had stolen their farm. She closed her eyes and saw details—exposed boards, once whitewashed, that time had weathered to reveal spots on the wood that looked like contusions on thin, pale skin. The house sat a half-mile from the edge of town, hunkered behind a disintegrating picket fence and hemmed in by discarded machinery: rotting wagons, rusting iron, a buck rake missing a wheel, and a Mormon hay derrick. There sat a settling pile of dead cows and calves— winterkill—dumped there and picked over by birds and insects until all that remained were tattered hides pulled taut over bleached bones. The dead animals were so far gone they did not smell much anymore, not unless the wind was blowing from the wrong direction.

Peter refused to live in that house. "I'm old enough to be on my own. I'm heading west to California. I'll get a job when I get there. I'll send money home every month."

Apparently there was plenty of work. He did send money home, and that was what Red and her mother lived on. Ann's health was not good, but she did what she could for as long as she could. In truth her body never recovered from her bout with the flu or from losing Marvin. It reached the point where she was bedridden.

Red cared for her mother and continued to attend school. On the last day before Christmas vacation the teacher told her, "I want you to take home the tree."

It was the teacher's custom to allow the poorest child to have the classroom tree. She told her teacher, "Mother would never take a handout, not from you, not from anybody."

That year Christmas at the Durkee house consisted of paper chains and cutout angels Red made and strung around the dingy shack. She planned a special gift for her mother and went to the mercantile store where she selected apples from a bin, carefully choosing apples that were round and smooth, firm, without blemishes or bruises. She peeled, cored and sliced the flawless apples and sprinkled on sugar and cinnamon. While they absorbed the sweetness and spices, she began making the dough, running in often to her mother's bedside and asking directions.

She measured flour and salt, cut in the lard, sprinkled on cold water, stirred with a fork, and worked the dough with her fingers. When the dough had a uniform consistency she divided it into equal halves, sprinkled flour on the breadboard, and stretching to use the rolling pin, flattened the dough into thin layers. After greasing a tin pie pan, she laid dough on the bottom, added the filling, placed the other half of the flattened dough on top and pinched the edges together. She was ready to put the pie in the oven when her mother whispered to her, saying, "Be sure to punch holes in the top with a fork. That way, as it cooks, the gas that builds up can escape."

While the pie baked, Red hovered around the wood stove and when the piecrust turned golden brown she took the pie from the oven and set it on a rack to cool. The pie was as perfect as the apples that had gone into the filling. But when it came time to eat the pie, Ann was too ill to try so much as a single bite.

"That's all right. Tomorrow you'll feel better. It'll taste just as good then."

She continued to care for her mother; rising early each morning, using the hand pump on the back porch to fill a bucket with water, carrying it inside and lifting it onto the wood stove. When the water was warm, she filled a basin on a table beside her mother's bed. If Ann was feeling up to it, she washed herself and if not, Red did it for her. She sat with her mother in the long afternoons and shared what had gone on at school. While her mother slept, she washed clothes and hung them on the line to dry. She dusted, mopped and performed all the other necessary household chores. She became an adequate cook, with an amazing ability to stretch and stretch their measly food budget. Meat was a delicacy, and on those special occasions when it was on the menu, she bought whatever the butcher had on sale. Leftovers were placed in the cool box, a washtub hung outside the kitchen window.

Once in a great while, a neighbor took pity on the sick woman and child and dropped off a gallon of milk, a brick of freshly churned butter, a pie or a plate of cinnamon rolls still warm from the oven. More than likely, the generous neighbor said something like, "We had extra," or "I was planning on company but they couldn't make it and I didn't want this to go to waste." In that way their generosity was disguised and Ann did not have to acknowledge it for what it was, a handout.

┼┼┼┼┼┼

Spring, as it always does in Montana, came slowly and grudgingly. A warm south wind arrived to lick at the snowdrifts. They began to recede; moisture collecting into puddles and bleeding off to feed the Yellowstone River and eventually to join forces with the muddy Missouri. Poking through the shrinking piles of snow, lively crocuses emerged in tiny bursts of colors. In protected areas hyacinths soon bloomed and cast their sweet fragrance on the wind. But again, winter returned as it always seemed to with a fresh dusting of snow.

Red was perched on the seat of the rusting buck rake and the metal sent piercing cold through the seat of her trousers. An unseen dove, down in the thicket of red-barked willows, bounced a series of clear, round notes sounding like a soft stick tapping a hollow log, *tuu-tuu-tu-tu*. The call hung in the crisp air for a long moment and then from a distance came an answering call. Again and again the anxious declarations were made, the notes becoming closer together, more resonant and insistent. At last a pair of doves flashed overhead, flying wing tip to wing tip, silhouetted against the golden sky.

Red was happy for the birds. They had found each other, but their coming together only seemed to amplify her personal loneliness. Her father was dead and buried in the ground. That afternoon her sick mother had joined him. Her death, in a way, was a blessing. She had been ailing for so long and had suffered so much. Now Red sat on the cold metal seat and asked God, "Why are you doing this to me? Why do I have to face so many tragedies? All I ever wanted was a father, a mother and a home. Is that too much to ask for?"

The setting sun slid behind the horizon and disappeared. The evening grew steadily colder. Once more the doves flitted across heaven, and after they were gone the sky was empty and flat. Tarnished gold clouds became a sober gray, turning charcoal and finally blackness prevailed. Stars appeared and danced in the night. Red shivered and bit her lower lip in an effort to stop her trembling.

┌┼┼┼┼┼┐

On the far side of town, Ed Hall was in a meeting with Ralph Thurman, telling the attorney, "Things worked out just like you said they would. We both made money. But I feel bad."

Thurman pushed himself away from his desk. "Bad about what?"

"The girl; her momma's dead and now she's all alone."

"You? A guilty conscience?" Mr. Thurman chided his partner with an exaggerated shake of his head.

"I suppose I shouldn't feel guilty. I gave them a place to live." Ed puffed on his cigar.

"Big of you." Mr. Thurman smiled.

"I didn't have to do that."

"No, you certainly didn't. But I tell you, I have a hard time fathoming, after all the deals you and I have put together over the years, this is the one that gets you. You let that cute redhead tug your heart strings."

Ed said nothing. He and his wife had never had children. He wished they had. Finally he said, "So what?"

"Okay, since apparently you feel some sort of responsibility, I'll draw up papers making you the child's legal guardian. Just don't take her in. Board her out. That way she doesn't interfere

125

in your everyday life and your conscience remains as chaste as a virgin's heart."

On his way home, Ed stopped at the boarding house and spoke to Mrs. Braxton, telling her, "I want you to board Red Durkee. I'll pay. She's a good kid. Have her work. She's plenty old enough to set the table, do chores and such. Only condition is, you leave my name out of it. This arrangement is strictly between you and me. Understood?"

Mrs. Braxton understood perfectly. She invited Red to move in with her, but lied to the girl and told her that she would have to pay her room and board by working. Red, who had lived at the boarding house when her father and mother became ill, was only too happy to move in because Mrs. Braxton's boarding house was the only place she had ever lived that had running water and indoor plumbing.

Every afternoon Red came straight from school, changed clothes in her room and went downstairs to the kitchen to help Mrs. Braxton with dinner. She set the table, helped serve and clear the dishes after the boarders had eaten. While the dishes soaked, she was allowed to help herself to leftovers. Then as soon as she finished eating, she was expected to wash, dry and put away the dishes. Only when the chores were finished was she allowed to go to her room, tackle her homework, or read a little, before falling asleep from exhaustion. At 5 o'clock each morning Mrs. Braxton was pounding on her door again, waking Red and forcing her to start yet another day. Month after month the dreary routine repeated itself.

Nina Kirsch moved into the boarding house and occupied the room adjoining Red's. She was a heavyset woman with grayish yellow hair pulled back into a severe bun. She favored roomy house dresses. Loose skin flecked with age spots hung in unsightly folds above her elbows. She sat in her room and smoked cigarettes, sucking in the smoke with purpose and expelling it toward the ceiling in a filthy, gray stream. At night she was stricken with such dreadful fits of coughing that Red was often awakened. One night in particular, the coughing became so excruciatingly fierce, followed by an eerie silence, that Red became fearful for her neighbor's well-being. She crawled from under the covers, padded barefoot into the hall and tapped her knuckles politely against the wooden door.

"It's open," Nina rasped.

Nina was in bed, propped up against a small mountain of pillows, her face illuminated by the light of a wooden match she held to the tip of a Lucky Strike cigarette. She choked on the first puff, sending forth a cloud of acrid smoke, but tried again and successfully filled her lungs with poison. As an afterthought, she blew out the match.

"Dearie, please turn on the light," Nina said. And when the room brightened from a floor lamp that puddled light around it, Nina's gravelly voice asked, "Whatsoever brings you to my room this time of the night?"

"I was concerned about you."

Nina laid the cigarette in a well-used silver ashtray as thin tears squeezed from the corners of her eyes. She reached to the nightstand and took a wad of tissue, dabbed at her eyes and blew her nose fiercely before picking up the cigarette once more. She flashed a weak and embarrassed smile and said, "Don't you ever take up this filthy habit."

"I won't," Red promised.

The two unlikely neighbors talked that night, and from then on they visited regularly. Nina smoked and coughed and talked about her past. If Red hung around long enough, Nina brought out a shoebox crammed with photographs. There were pictures of her, her deceased husband, family members, friends, homes, automobiles, wagons, buggies, chickens, turkeys, bucking broncs, prized horses, cattle, sheep and favorite dogs. The box camera had recorded each image with startling clarity. Its accurate and honest eye captured young faces imprinted with glimmers of pride, surprise, ambition, promise, hope and laughter. Later photographs presented the stark realities of dreams that died slowly—grief, sorrow, pain and abject poverty—all etched in various shades of fading sepia.

She thumbed the photographs, stopping and lingering from time-to-time on a particular photograph. She talked about places where fences stretched to meet the sky and told of turning virgin sod, rains that did not come, lightning storms igniting the sky, floods drowning crops, crops lost to hailstorms and fires that had swept across the prairies. She recited the names of horses. "That's Dutch and Dusty. This one's Ned. Polly and Dolly they were quite the team. That's Beauty. She was my saddle horse, an absolute darling; used to feed her grain right out of my hand. She was careful not to bite me. Oh Lordy, all the places Beauty an' I've seen. My, oh my!" And she told about dogs, all of them long since dead, just like the horses.

Each time she came to the photographs of a little girl dressed in ruffles and ribbons and bows, her eyes moistened. When she spoke, her voice quavered. "My sweet little Lila. She gave me trouble at birth, don't ya know. Couldn't have no more after Lila was born.

"We lost her. I was there when it happened. River runnin' flood. Log hit up alongside the ferry. Lila she done got knocked overboard. Washed away an' wasn't nothin' nobody could do. No savin' her. That heartless ol' Missouri pulled her down an' carried her away. Never was able to have a proper burial for my precious Lila. That was the hardest thing of all."

Red listened intently to all the stories. She heard them a dozen times, a hundred times and more. Nina said that after her husband passed away from pneumonia, she tried desperately to hang on to the homestead. But what could she do? She was one woman alone on the frontier. The sheep men knew it and moved in, driving their sheep onto her fields in the middle of the night and moving on before daylight.

"That first winter after my husband passed, I plain run out of food. So I bundled up—was a blizzard a blowin' in—an' rode four miles ta the nearest neighbor. He was a meanspirited ol' man, said he didn't have no food ta spare. I went two miles farther on ta the next neighbor. They was a family with nine kids ta feed, but they shared. They give me beans an' cornmeal. That's what pulled me through.

"Come spring I planted a garden. Had ta dip water outta the crick an' haul it more'n a mile in the back of the wagon. Along about the middle of August the crick dried up and that was that. I harvested what I could an' let it go at that.

"The year after, a cloud of grasshoppers come an' cleaned me out. They even got down into the root cellar an' ate the little dab of seed corn I had stored there. Come fall the wind blew somethin' fierce. Wasn't nothin' ta stop it. It skimmed off the topsoil and blowed it away ta Timbuktu. That was the last straw. I walked away. Come ta town. Got me a job and stayed with it 'til I couldn't work no more. An' here I am."

The two friends fulfilled each other's needs. Nina gave Red a sense of family, of roots and belonging. Nina found in Red the daughter she had lost. When Nina was diagnosed with tuberculosis, it was Red who wrote a letter to the Montana State Sanatorium requesting they add Nina's name to the patient waiting list.

⁜⁜⁜⁜⁜⁜

Red came waltzing into Nina's room and found the woman holding an envelope. Red inquired if the letter was from the sanatorium. Nina replied, "Don't rightly know, my eyes they don't be so good t'day."

Red opened the envelope and read the letter. *"This letter is notification of a vacancy at the Montana State TB Sanatorium. Please notify by wire if you are in a position to accept. It is impossible to hold a vacancy more than a few days. Yours truly, Dr. Norman Taft."*

The following day, while Red was in school, Nina was helped aboard the westbound passenger train. A few weeks later, Red received a letter from her friend. The writing was scribbled and hard to read but she managed.

Dearest Red,

I think about you often, miss your visits and miss my room there.

They keep me in bed day plus night. Serve me meals in bed. What do you think of that? They won't let me smoke and I ain't suppose to be writin' no letters since they have me flattened out and not to get up 'cept to go to the bathroom. Even still I get to meet lots of new folks. Will write again when they move me to the 'Up' building. That's where you can get up from bed once in awhile.

Your good friend,

Nina.

It was a month before another letter arrived.

Dearest Red,

They sent me to the 'Up' building which means I go to the dining hall for lunch and don't have to be back in bed til 4 o'clock. They let me stroll around some and talk all I want. Every Saturday afternoon they bring in a movie. I seen Doug Fairbanks and Mary Pickford, they got hitched, don't ya know. I seen Charlie Chaplin, twice. This week they played Gloria Swanson in "Her

Gilded Cage." She was quite the flirt. Turned out to be a real tearjerker.

The woman who sleeps in the bed next to me, Geneva, she is a friend of mine, she had to have surgery. They took out a rib so her lung wouldn't collapse. She is in a bad way. They took her back to the 'In' building.

Lately we been sleeping on the screened-in porch. We take hot water bottles and lots of extra blankets. It just smells so much better out there. Ain't all mediciney.

I'll write again.

As always, your friend,

Nina.

P.S. Just got word about Geneva. They say she died.

Red wrote to Nina, but the envelope was returned as undeliverable. A line was drawn through Nina's name and address and a single word had been scrawled there, *deceased*. Red thought, but she was doing so well. They had moved her to the 'Up' building. She was on the mend. She couldn't have died.

Yet another death was almost more than she could endure. That night she spoke to God once again, asking Him, "Why do you keep taking everyone I love?"

She felt a responsibility to share the painful news with Mrs. Braxton. She also wanted to ask her landlady for a favor. She thought it best to find the most opportune moment and hurried through her chores. Mrs. Braxton was seated comfortably at the kitchen table, drinking lukewarm tea, smoking a Wings cigarette and reading a bit of titillating yellow journalism from one of William Randolph Hearst's tabloid newspapers.

"Excuse me, Mrs. Braxton."

Mrs. Braxton continued to read until she reached the bottom of the page. Then she looked up and acknowledged the interruption with a stern, "What is it?"

"I thought you would want to know, Nina died. It was unexpected."

"Those things happen."

"I suppose so. We live and we die," Red said morbidly.

Mrs. Braxton returned to reading. When she realized Red was still standing there, she let out an audible sigh and inquired, "Something else to tell me?"

"I was walking home from school today and Mrs. Putnam, from up the road, she has this cute little bummer lamb she's having to feed with a bottle. She said I could have it if it was okay with you. She will give me the milk. What do you think, Mrs. Braxton?

Mrs. Braxton exhaled smoke, "About what?"

"About me getting a lamb? I'll take good care of it. You won't even know it's around. Please, oh please."

"I don't care what you do, as long as you do your chores. Now go away and leave me alone."

Red constructed a makeshift pen and lean-to from boards she scavenged around town. Not a single nail went into the project. The wood was held together with twine and wire. When it was complete, she walked to Mrs. Putnam's and carried home the long-tailed lamb. She placed the baby on a bed of straw in the lean-to. Every few hours she heated a bottle on the stove and fed the little lamb. She named him Dancer because, while the lamb suckled, it moved its feet as rapidly as a dancer. She even left school during lunch to feed Dancer and the lamb was always happy to see her. He stood spraddle-legged and wagged his thin, white clumsy tail.

The following weekend, Mrs. Putnam, who was of Basque descent, came to castrate Dancer. She performed the operation by splitting the scrotum with her teeth, biting the cords and spitting the testicles onto the ground. The long tail was bobbed with one quick whack with a hatchet on a chopping block. Red daubed Mercurochrome on the open wounds and cuddled Dancer, stroking his wool, telling him how sorry she was, kissing the top of his head and holding him tightly to her chest. All the love she had to give was focused on Dancer.

Dancer outgrew the bottle and switched to grazing on spring grasses. The rains soon stopped, summer dug in its heels and the succulent grasses shriveled in their sheaths. Even the weeds toughened up in order to survive. Red took Dancer for long walks along the river, where a thin line of green clung to the shoreline. The lamb nibbled the tops of the best forage. Wherever she went, the lamb followed. She hiked uptown to fetch this or that for Mrs. Braxton and her lamb trailed behind, patiently waiting outside the stores.

All through the long summer of warm days and blue skies, she and the lamb were inseparable. Then school started once again and before long sandstone skies signaled the arrival of early storms sweeping down from out of the northern regions.

Then came the day when she came home from school to find the sheep pen empty, the gate standing open. A stout wave of panic washed over her, making it difficult for her to breathe. She ran around the house like a frantic mother, calling, "Dancer, Dancer, where are you Dancer?"

She finally noticed the rope used to tie the gate closed had been cut. It was at that precise moment that Mrs. Braxton appeared on the porch, fixed Red with an icy glare, and scolded her, saying, "Be quiet. You're disturbing my boarders."

"What did you do with Dancer?"

"Exactly what should be done with a fat lamb. I sent him to market, that's what."

Red turned and ran. She ran until she collapsed from exhaustion. She lay sobbing into the thirsty sand. That night she never went to her room, instead choosing to huddle in a hollow carved by spring runoff. She lay on a bed of golden leaves discarded by a towering cottonwood tree and pulled the leaves over her as a cool wind swirled and nipped at her. A lonely owl sat on a branch in a dead tree calling *whoo-whoo-whoo* and coyotes serenaded the star-spangled sky.

Mrs. Braxton notified Ed Hall of Red's absence. He drove around looking for her, found her aimlessly pitching round stones off the flat, reflective sheen of the Yellowstone River. He cut the engine and it gave off a series of ticks and pings as it began to cool. He cranked down the window and cigar smoke oozed from the opening.

"Kid, you best hop in."

When she did not respond he grumbled, kicked open the door of the Packard and swung his feet to the ground. As he drew near he noticed she was taller than he remembered.

"Mrs. Braxton told me what happened. I suppose she should have talked to you beforehand, but she didn't. Can't change the past.

"I want you to go back to the boarding house. I've got it all worked out. Mrs. Braxton won't hold no grudge on account of you running away and neglecting your chores. She's agreed to pay you half the value of your lamb."

With that declaration made, he tossed the well-chewed butt of his cigar on the ground and crushed it flat beneath his boot heel. Red remained silent. As near as she could tell her only option was to do as Ed Hall directed. Reluctantly she got in his automobile. He drove her back to the boarding house. Mrs. Braxton acted as if nothing out of the ordinary had transpired, and then to reinstate her authority, she directed Red to, "Run downtown and fetch me a pack of Wings."

Mr. Logan was standing by the window of his mercantile store when Red walked through the doorway. He smiled and cheerfully asked, "I don't see Mr. Dancer with you today. Did he find a stack of loose hay and get side-tracked along the way?"

"That mean old witch sold him and some man hauled him away and butchered him."

"I'm so sorry. I had no idea ... absolutely no idea. Here," he offered her a cinnamon stick. "Take this. Please."

She suddenly made up her mind, and instead of returning to the boarding house she marched to Ed Hall's office, barged in and informed him, "I ain't goin' back. That's all there is to it. I ain't."

"Fine," Ed said. "Anyway, just so you know, after your momma died, I was appointed your legal guardian. Like it or not, what I say goes." He dug his wallet from his hind pocket, fished through the bills, selected a ten spot and handed it to Red. "When you were a kid you weren't much trouble, but the older you've gotten, the more bothersome you've become. I'm done bein' your guardian. Use this here to buy yourself a ticket, take the train to Helena and enroll in reform school. I'll contact 'em, an' tell 'em you're incorrigible."

Red had difficulty understanding how the man who had been her father's partner, the man who had cheated them out of the farm, could have become her legal guardian. How did that happen? What was a guardian supposed to do? She thought a guardian should at least be someone who looked out for another person's best interests. As far as she knew, he had never acted in that capacity. And now he was shoving ten bucks at her and telling her to take the train to Helena and enroll in reform school?

As she left the office, she thought back to when her father died and again felt the overwhelming sense of loss. She recalled the way blue snow drifted around her father's gray granite headstone. *Rest in Peace*. She remembered the months of caring for her mother. And she thought about Nina, and Dancer.

Each death had stolen something from Red, robbing her of her innocence, leaving her with the nagging bitterness of isolation. God was punishing her, she was sure of that, and He was taking away everyone and anything that had any meaning. She thought that she did not want to care about someone, or something, ever again.

"I don't want to love, because I don't want that taken from me."

┣┿┿┿┿┿┫

Red purchased a ticket to Helena just as Ed Hall had instructed she must do. She stepped aboard the train and soon the warmth of the late fall heat wave, the gentle sway of the Pullman car and the elegance of the soft, rich upholstery worked to make her drowsy. She teetered on the knife-edged brink of sleep, thinking about what awaited her at the end of the ride—reform school—and anticipating there would be bad girls there; troubled girls, girls with wild hearts and loose morals. Just before Red fell asleep, she told herself, "If they try to make me wear a uniform, I'll run away. Swear I will."

She awoke with a start. It took a few seconds to recognize the train was slowing and the porter, a black man in a maroon suit with dangly gold epaulettes, was gently tapping her shoulder, repeating, "Missy, dis here's wha ya said yas gonna be gettin' off."

"Helena?" she questioned, "This is Helena?"

"Das right," he said, flashing a grin punctuated by a front tooth gleaming gold. He moved away. She wiggled herself to a less lackadaisical sitting position and drew a deep breath. Her nerve endings—exposed, raw and tender—fired and caused her to shiver. There was a thin coating of moisture on her forehead and upper lip and she used a handkerchief to mop it away. She indulged herself a bit by tipping back her head and wiping the front of her neck. She wished the cloth had been dipped in cold spring water. That would have been more refreshing.

The train shuddered to a stop. Sunlight reflected off a wooden platform. Heat shimmered in undulating waves. The depot manager's dog, a mongrel that typically greeted each arriving train with a wagging tail, was lazy in the heat and never bothered to move from his shady spot on the north side of the building. He lay sprawled on the ground, quivering tongue lolling from his mouth, chest pumping like a bellows.

She stood on the platform with her bag at her feet. The train pulled away. Black smoke belched from the tall smokestack. Steam pounded, metal screeched, and the heavy locomotive bowed the track in passing and drew the cars away until they looked, in the distance, like a toy train. Red still did not move. A boy on roller skates, hair blowing in the wind he created, whizzed past. That was the only movement. The oppressive heat of the day seemed to hold everything else firmly in place.

Eventually she picked up her tote and walked the short distance into town where she stopped at a soda fountain, set down her bag and crawled onto a high stool. She swung restlessly on the swivel stool, impatient to be served. Glancing down the row of empty stools, Red watched the young waitress take a last puff on a cigarette and lay the lipstick-laced butt onto an ashtray. Then she used a cocked wrist to push her glasses up into position on her hawk-like nose.

As the waitress drew near, Red complimented her, saying, "I like your glasses."

After checking her reflection in the mirror behind the fountain, and smacking her lips to bring pink to the surface, the waitress replied, "It ain't like I need cheaters, understand. It's just I've been told they make me look intelligent. I don't want anyone to get the impression I'm a Dumb Dora or anything of the sort."

She gave her customer a quick appraisal, and from the way the girl with the red hair was dressed—a boyish plaid cotton short-sleeve shirt, trousers, and hair pulled back into a severe ponytail—it was pretty obvious she was some hick from the sticks. The waitress decided to have a little fun. She asked, "Know what's under a pony tail?"

Red self-consciously reached back and fingered her ponytail. She shook her head.

"Sure you do; a horse's butt." The waitress laughed. "Just kiddin' ya, buttercup. Feedin' you a bunch of applesauce... you know, banana oil, hokum, bunk, baloney. I wasn't makin' fun; just havin' fun. Lordy, lordy, we could use a little fun in this one-horse town." Her tone changed. "You come in on the train?"

"Yeah," Red said.

"This is the last place I'd get off. If I was ta go somewhere, I'd go ta Hollywood. That's California, don't ya know. With the right outfit on, I'm every bit as good lookin' as Gloria Swanson. Ever see *Gilded Cage*? Good movie." She pulled up the hemline of her white cotton uniform skirt, exposing dimpled knees. "I got nice legs, don't you think?"

Red guessed so. She shrugged.

The waitress kept talking. "A cake-eater, you know, a real ladies' man, come in here fresh from Cal-if-or-nia. Said I had the best gams—that's what he called 'em, gams—that he ever seen. That's word-for-word what he said to me."

Releasing her grip, the material fell away and the dress swayed back into position just below her knees. She unwrapped a stick of gum that she folded over and promptly popped in her mouth. She chewed noisily.

"Said he was a top cheese in show business. Named off at least a dozen stars he knew personally: John Barrymore, Rudolph Valentino, Greta Garbo, Ronald Colman, Doug Fairbanks, Joan Crawford.... I told him I planned ta visit California an' he said to me when I got there, ta look him up. Said he'd get me into movies. Gave me his business card, he did. How 'bout you? Where you goin'?"

Red did not see a need to hide the truth. "Reform school."

"That so? What'd you do?"

"Nothin'."

"Everybody I ever heard of that got sent there done robbed someone or been caught in a compromisin' situation."

"Not me. I didn't do nothin'."

"Pure as driven snow. So, tell me, what can I get ya?"

"Guess...umm, chocolate malt."

"One chocolate malt comin' up!" The waitress turned her back, and lacking anything of substance to say, she made small talk. "Pretty hot. Don't ever remember it bein' this hot so late in the year. Guess you could use somethin' cold."

Red indulged herself with the malt and watched through the window as a swanky Cadillac passed, followed a moment later by mismatched horses pulling a wagon. A wild conglomeration of kids chased after the wagon, caught the tailboard and hitched a ride, dragging their feet and creating a boil of dust. Minutes passed. The silent white dust sifted and began to settle. Red spooned the last of the chocolate malt into her mouth, swung off her stool, put change on the counter and prepared to leave.

The waitress, who had resumed her position at the end of the fountain, called, "One of these days I'm blowin' this town, and when I do, look out world!" She flashed a toothy grin, lit another cigarette and blew smoke into the still air. "See ya 'round the bend, sugarplum."

139

An insurgent blast of cool, dry air, born somewhere over the Arctic, had slipped south, and at twenty thousand feet over Montana ran smack dab into the scorcher of a day. Thunderheads boiled like growing cathedrals in the sky. On the ground, an insolent wind puffed into existence. As Red returned to the street, a few loose ends of her paprika-colored hair blew about and tickled her face. She retied her ponytail while window-shopping, moving aimlessly from one storefront to the next. When she ran out of buildings she crossed over and retraced her steps on the other side of the street. Sweet fragrances—the pungent taste of evergreen and the more discriminating and subtle smells of deciduous trees, flowers and damp earth—rode the coattails of the swirling wind.

Translucent clouds with opaque bellies overran the blue sky, and at long last the glowing citadel sent diagonal curtains of dazzling vapor toward earth, a cursory warning of the storm to come. Fat, warm raindrops spanked her face. She tipped her chin upward to savor the effect. Moisture slid over her skin. Apparently the rain enjoyed it so much it abruptly evaporated, to go back into the sky and do it all over again.

※※※※※※

She found herself in a dank room with only one small window, seated in a straight-backed chair. Her hands were folded submissively on her lap. Standing in front of her, towering over her, was a big-boned woman with eyes like lumps of coal pressed into a block of fleshy cookie dough. When the woman spoke, her voice was husky and seemed to emanate from somewhere deep inside her bulky frame.

"Maude Jenkins," the woman said. "I run this here outfit. I expected the rain would bring you in. I knew you were coming since I had a wire to that effect from a Mr. Hall. Did some checking around, I did. Spoke to your teacher from home, Mr.

Perry. He didn't have a single bad word to say about you. Said you were a good student, gifted with numbers. Said you were an orphan and a responsible young lady. In fact, he said he wished he had a whole school of girls just like you.

"I must admit something to you, Miss Durkee. You are the first. In the 17 years I've held this position, I've never before had a girl who came here and checked herself in of her own free will. The girls we get are sent here by the court or dumped off by parents who have reached their wit's end. Nobody wants my girls. Folks don't. Teachers don't. Preachers don't. Sheriffs don't.

"My girls have been branded, had it burned right into their skin with a red hot iron—*incorrigible*. What I do is put a roof over their heads and food in their bellies. And then, by friendship or by force, we make them into productive members of society."

After Maude had had her say, she escorted Red to her room. It was a long, narrow shoebox-like affair with three wooden desks side-by-side against one wall. On the opposite side were bunk beds stacked three high. There was a window at the far end of the room. Red was drawn to that window and stood there in a pool of ashen light. She gazed through the pitted glass and between vertical wrought iron bars. The view was a panorama of shingled rooftops, and in the distance smokestacks vomited brown sludge into the drab sky. Farther yet, in the distance, just below the canopy of low clouds, were foothills leading to the Rocky Mountains. The topography seemed to end there.

Red had given up her freedom—in her mind she had no option but to go along with what Ed Hall told her she must do—and now she realized she might never have the opportunity to walk where the hills melted together, or explore the long draw carved by a stream where herons stood on skinny legs knee-deep in back eddies waiting with infinite patience to catch minnows that flashed quicksilver. Nor would she have the chance to visit the slough of stagnant water and waving cattails at the edge of town where bullfrogs bellowed. She was mulling all this over in her mind when she became aware of whispers in the hall, girls' voices. She caught quick snippets of their conversation.

"She done signed herself in!"

"Wasn't nobody standin' over her with a whip makin' her do it."

"I sure as hell never woulda done that."

"Poor thing must not have a full limit of fish on her stringer."

There was a burst of laughter, the door flew open and two girls tumbled into the room like clowns onto a stage. They looked to be a couple years older than Red, but it was hard to tell. The taller of the two had ebony hair cropped close around her ears. Her gray-green eyes sparkled wickedly. She was wearing a fashionable blue dress with white buttons running from neck to waistline, blue Holeproof hose and black lace-up leather boots. She flung herself on the lower bunk, patted down her dress and said, "I'm Zelda."

The shorter of the two had blue eyes and blonde hair, was a few pounds overweight, average looking and wearing farmer coveralls with one shoulder strap hanging loosely. Her appearance gave the impression she was somewhere between a tomboy and a tramp. She leaped onto the bunk above Zelda, craned her neck like an eagle on its nest and said, "I'm Bertie, and Toots, your bed is topside." She gave a playful giggle and pointed to the top bunk.

"I go by Red." She turned back to the window, concentrating not on the view, but her first impression of her roommates. They flounced, defiantly chomped gum and were like a couple of wild jokers tossed from a fresh deck of playing cards. She thought these girls were certainly going to spice up her life and make it a whole lot livelier. She liked them immediately. She might have missed having a typical childhood, but she told herself she was going to make the most of her teenage years.

"I'm dying for a smoke. Hey Red, you smuggle in any cigs?"

"Bet ya a sawbuck she don't smoke. Ever try it, hon'?"

"Never."

"We may just have to corrupt you," Bertie said with a giggle.

That night, after the lights were extinguished, the girls stayed awake, sharing stories and secrets. Red looked over the edge of the top bunk. An electric light hanging in the courtyard was the source of a coppery glow that leaked into the room and bathed the room in a gloomy light. She could see Bertie in the bunk below. Her blonde hair was fluffy. She had not yet outgrown her baby fat and her skin was ruddy and given to outbreaks and blemishes. Her eyes were thickly lashed.

Bertie claimed her personal problems began and ended with her father. He was the sole reason she was sent to live in what she referred to as "this hell-hole of a reform school." She went on to say, "My old man's mean as all get out; used to horsewhip me for no good reason, none at all. Least little thing set him off. He'd grab up whatever was handy; beat me with the buggy whip, lines from the harness, with switches and boards. One time he beat me with an axe handle.

"I ain't never done nothing big. Never stuck up no one, swiped money, kilt no one, nothing like that. Whenever I got in trouble, I was just fooling around, having me some fun."

Bertie said she was born and raised in Missoula, Montana. Her father was a narrow-minded logger who understood crosscut saws, side notching and the art of wedging a tree to fall in a certain, predetermined direction. He never understood his wife, and most assuredly never understood his daughter.

He claimed she was a wild child, crazy, reckless and goin' straight ta hell.

According to Bertie, her father was a strict disciplinarian who thought he could beat good sense into her. But each time he whipped her, she rebelled all the more.

"What made him send you here?" Red had wanted to know.

"Had me a boyfriend, Billy Morgan, handsome as sin he was. We used to sneak off to the hay barn, the woods, wherever, and fool around, don't you know. This one afternoon my old man caught me wrapped in the arms of Billy Morgan. We weren't doin' much. Fact is, we had most all our clothes on.

"But my old man lets loose with his buggy whip. Whips us both within an inch of our lives. Billy goes runnin' off like a dog shot with rock salt. Then my old man turns his meanness on me. Whips me front and back. I got scars to prove it. I'll show you one of these days.

"I tried runnin' away. Hitched me a ride up to Lolo Pass with a travelin' salesman. He was a nice fellow, said he wanted to take care of me. We were havin' ourselves a bite to eat at a diner when the county sheriff comes walkin' in and makes me go out and get my things. Everything I owned was wrapped in a pillowcase. Sheriff runs the salesman off with a warning to never pick up no young girls on the highway, never again. Then the sheriff he takes me home. But my mean old man says he don't want nothin' more to do with me. Says he's done washed his hands of me. Mama she cries, but there ain't nothin' she can do 'bout it. The sheriff has no choice but to bring me here. That's the way the ball bounces."

The two roommates were as different as night and day. Zelda wore colorful clothes; saddle shoes and smart dresses with collars and wide belts. She surrounded herself with movie magazines and told a story she read in *Real Life* about Joan Crawford and her movie *Our Dancing Daughters*, where Miss

Crawford drank what she called giggle water, smoked cigarettes and engaged in necking and petting parties. Zelda said that was where she learned to dance the Charleston, crossing and uncrossing her hands on her knees just like Miss Crawford. The film, about decadent youth, had made Zelda want to lead the flapper lifestyle. She thought herself to be as grown-up, and nearly as worldly, as Joan Crawford.

The other star Zelda loved to identify with was Clara Bow, the full-lipped, big-eyed, dimple-kneed gal who, born dirt poor in Brooklyn, had entered a beauty contest, won first prize and was whisked off to Hollywood. Her first bit part ended up on the cutting-room floor, but she persevered and soon won fame as the *It* girl. *It* was a suggestive word denoting a physical attractiveness, not necessarily beauty, but a raw animal magnetism that only a few women possess.

"Do you think I have *It*?" Zelda asked Red.

"I guess," Red said, not knowing what *It* meant.

For all her pretense, Zelda was from a family so poor she confided to Red, "Once a week, on Saturday night, we heated water over a wood stove and bathed. We all used the same water. I was fifth in line behind Uncle George. He was a pig farmer.

"When we lost the farm we hit the road. We had been living on pork and beans for two months and my daddy was so busted he didn't have two nickels to rub together. If he ever got hold of a two-bit piece it would've looked as big as a pancake to him. They dropped me off here, and I was tickled pink 'cause I knew I'd get three squares a day.

"But I won't be here forever. I do have my dreams, don't you know."

Once more she was Joan Crawford. Later she would be Clara Bow. She never did divulge how, coming from such a poor background, she could afford colorful clothes and movie

145

magazines. Red figured there had to be a story there, but she never inquired.

Just before the girls drifted off to sleep, Zelda said, "You know, Red, you got real pretty hair. If you was to have it cut and curled, and if you was to put on a nice dress and a little lipstick, you'd be cute enough not many boys could resist."

⋮⋮⋮⋮⋮⋮⋮

During that long winter the three girls became inseparable friends. On the first day of spring, when the dull sun emerged from behind a wall of transparent fog and began to show some vibrancy, it was Bertie who suggested, "We ought to break out and have ourselves some fun."

"What would we do?" Zelda wanted to know.

"Skip rocks across the pond," offered Red.

"Naw, way too civilized. I wanna have," Bertie spelled it out, "F-U-N" and addressing Zelda, said, "Remember that warehouse we heard about? The one that's supposed to have a stockpile of you-know-what? Let's have a look-see."

"I'm game," Zelda said.

They moved toward the door. Red looked after them anxiously and asked, "What about me?"

"You don't need an invite. Get poppin'."

Red tagged along with her older roommates, escaping through an unlocked side door in the kitchen and running to the rail yard. The warehouse they were searching for was rumored to have a distinctive row of high windows. Once they located the building, Bertie and Zelda hoisted Red onto their shoulders. She reached through a broken pane, turned the latch and pushed open the window. She inched herself up, squirmed through the narrow opening and dropped to the wooden floor. For a long moment she stood trying to get her bearings. Slender bars of sunlight slanted through narrow cracks in the board walls, illuminating particles of dust suspended above crates and boxes piled on top of each other. Red breathed in the dank air that reeked of grease and grime and generations of mice; smells seemingly intensified by the metallic screech and thunder of cars coupling as a train was being put together in the yard.

"Open up. Let us in," Zelda hissed, banging on the door. "Quick, 'fore someone sees us. Come on."

In a few swift strides, Red crossed the room, twisted the lock and threw open the door. Zelda and Bertie rushed inside and began tearing at the lids of wooden crates with a piece of pipe they found and used as a pry bar. In a crate labeled "Farm Machinery Parts" they discovered quart bottles of an amber liquid. Bertie worked a cork free, smelled the contents and took a long sip. She pursed her lips and gave a contented sigh. Zelda snatched away the bottle and took a thirsty gulp.

"What is it?" Red whispered.

"Hooch," Bertie said.

Red was unfamiliar with the word. Bertie stole the bottle back, "For cripesake, don't you know nothin'? Moonshine. Know what moonshine is?"

"Daddy owned a saloon. I know what moonshine is. I just never heard it called hooch. That's all."

"Have a swig." Bertie pushed the bottle toward Red.

Red brought the opening to her lips, swallowed a discreet amount and was surprised because there was hardly any taste to it. She took another sip and handed the bottle on to Zelda.

Within a few minutes, the girls were giggling and pushing the bottle back and forth between them. They swiped a second bottle, went outside, crossed eight sets of parallel train tracks and reached the safety of a low hill. They climbed it and took refuge under a spreading oak tree with a commanding view of the railroad yard and the surrounding countryside. The sun was midway through its afternoon arc. Birds were singing, insects buzzing. A monarch butterfly glided through the budding leaves, lit for an instant on Red's left shoulder and fluttered away.

"I think I'm getting ossified," Zelda slurred.

"Not me, I'm drunk as a skunk," Bertie said.

They drank and laughed and one-by-one the girls passed out and slept there under the tree on the top of the hill. Hours passed. Red, hearing the soft purr of the world around her, was the first to stir. She opened one eye and watched the tattered fragments of a cloud ride the jet stream high overhead. Then she must have dozed again, because when she came fully awake the sun had dropped from the sky. The only light was along the western flank of the horizon where a thin band of clouds were blushing a pale shade of phosphorescent pink. Evening sounds were audible: frogs, crickets, the murmur of wind in the grasses and the harsh whisper of leaves rubbing together. A cow mooed. A calf answered. A lonely train whistle split the evening air and a steam engine chugged noisily, beginning to pull away from Helena.

Red shook Bertie and Zelda awake. "We're in big trouble!"

Bertie sighed with indifference as her hands fumbled around on the ground until she retrieved one of the bottles. She tipped it up, took a quick gulp and replied, "We can't go back. Not unless we wanna take a ton of demerits an' get every crappy detail in the joint."

"Let's run away. That train's headed west. Let's hop it. I wanna go to California," Zelda said.

With the mention of California, Red felt a sharp twinge of sadness because Peter was in California and she had not seen her stepbrother in years. An impulse made her blurt, "I've got a brother living in Oakland. We can go there. I'm sure he'd put us up."

"What we waitin' for?" Bertie said. She was already on her feet and sprinting loose-legged down the hill toward the train that was now easing along the track. The others followed. Zelda whooped, "California, here we come!"

In the growing darkness, up on the hill under the oak tree, the last bottle tipped over; the contents drained out and were quickly absorbed into the dark, thirsty soil. The three girls reached the freight, and before it picked up too much speed, they climbed aboard a boxcar. For a while they sat in the doorway, riding like genuine hobos, but soon the dark shadows settled into the blackness of night. The girls moved inside and huddled together, sharing their warmth in a futile attempt to ward off the vicious wind that whistled through cracks in the dank interior of the boxcar. Red found the sensation of speed to be unsettling and there was a bedlam of vibrations and noise: clicking and clacking, chattering and clanking, squealing, and every so often, nerve-grating shrieks. Red was jostled by bumps, jars, shakes, rolls, sways, dips and jolts. Compounding her discomfort was an odd array of terrible smells: residue from damp grain, corn, potatoes, sawdust, ripe fruit and rotting animal hides.

"We should have gone back and taken our chances." Zelda shivered. "I never figured it'd get this cold."

"We're better off where we are," Bertie said. Giving a nervous little laugh, she added, "I gotta pee."

"Hang your fanny outside," Zelda suggested.

"No way! What if I was to fall? I don't mind dying, but I'll be damned if they'll find me with my coveralls 'round my ankles. Guess I have to hold it, but I hope we stop pretty soon."

"Red, how you doin'? You're so quiet," Zelda said.

"I was just remembering a pair of red long johns I got from Santa one Christmas and was wishing I had them with me now."

"If I had a wish," Zelda responded, "I'd wish for a down comforter and something pretty to put on in the morning. Why didn't I bring a brush and some toothpaste, lipstick and eye shadow? God, I'm thirsty. Anybody else thirsty?"

"I am."

"Me, too."

Zelda tried plowing new ground. "I wonder what kind of men we'll meet in California? I want a rich one who'll buy me things and pamper me; someone who can pull a few strings and get me into pictures. I'll make it. You just wait and see if I don't. A year from now, I'll be under studio contract, live in a palace by the sea and have a driver take me places in a Lincoln Coach Brougham just like Ethel Jackson. What are you going to do when you see my face 20 feet tall on the silver screen?"

"Throw you kisses," Red teased.

There was a particular moment when all the accustomed noises ceased. In that instant Red was sure she heard a cough from the far end of the boxcar. Then the train sounds returned with a rush and it was impossible for her to tell. Later another strange moment of quiet returned, and this time Red was almost sure she detected breathing; the harsh, raspy noise old men make. She strained her eyes, but could not see into the darkness except up near the top of the boxcar where she could make out pulses of starlight.

Zelda must have felt Red's tenseness because she whispered, "What's the matter?"

In a hushed tone Red said, "Heard something."

Bertie, not bothering to lower her voice, said, "What?"

"Someone," whispered Red, "Over there, across from us. I heard him cough; scrape his shoe on the floor, something. Listen, maybe you'll hear him."

After a long moment Bertie blurted, "I don't hear nothin'."

Zelda directed a whispered question toward Red. "You sure?"

"Think so," Red said.

"I'll have a look see," Bertie said. She got up, and a moment later returned, whispering, "Oh my God. You're right. Someone is there."

"Who's there?" Red demanded.

There was a stirring; an odd scuffling that came from the far wall. The sound of shoe leather scraping on wood came nearer. A match was lit—a match held in cupped hands—the flame illuminating a man's face framed by uncombed silver hair; scruffy white stubble on the chin and canyons of slack skin around the corners of his eyes.

"Railroad Bill," the old man said, "at your service." He grinned. He only had a few scraggly teeth. The match went out.

"How long you been there?" Bertie asked the darkness.

"All the way from Omaha. Pray tell, what do I owe the distinct honor of having three maidens accompanying me on my travels?"

Finding her voice once again, Red announced, "We're going to California."

"Sounded like Hollywood is acallin'."

"You could've had the decency to let us know you were here," Bertie said. "You alone?"

"Reckon so," Bill said. "That's the way I ramble. Big enough job just looking out for me. Don't need anyone else tagging along."

He moved away as he continued to talk. "I take it from your conversations that none of you have experience riding the rails. Little word of advice—lot warmer up front where I am—wind don't blow near so bad up here. Join me if you like. Plenty of room."

The girls quietly discussed it among themselves and concluded Railroad Bill was harmless. They moved to the front of the boxcar, but sat a cautious distance away from the old man. They traveled that way through the night, not talking.

Red, who was wedged tightly between the other two girls, awoke as the train began to slow. The interior of the boxcar was not as dark as it had been, but remained as dreary as gray muslin. However, there was sufficient light to make out shapes and Red looked in the direction of the old man. A discarded blanket marked where he had slept. He stood a few steps away, stretching, trying to work the kinks out of his spine. He sensed he was being watched and turned. Perhaps he saw a glint from Red's open eyes because he addressed her with a rather cheerful, "Morning."

"Where are we?"

"Comin' into Dillon," Bill said. "Most likely stop for a couple hours, maybe more. They'll add cars. Not many bulls around these parts so you don't need worry. But to play it safe we'll drop off before we get to the yard. You can stretch your legs a bit, grab a bite to eat and we'll catch her on the west side when she pulls out."

Bertie came awake and whispered, "Thank God we're stopping. I gotta pee so bad I'm about to explode."

In the town of Dillon the girls pooled their money and at a place called Mom's Homestead Café they bought one bowl of pea soup and a cup of coffee. They shared the soup and took turns drinking coffee until Mom refused to refill the cup. The runaway girls hurried to the far end of town and hid in the woods near the tracks.

Before long the engineer gave a series of lighthearted toots, the smokestack belched black soot, and the drive wheels of the locomotive spun in search of traction. Railroad Bill stood in the doorway of a boxcar, motioning for the girls to make a run for it. He offered each, in turn, a hand up.

Having put a little something warm in their stomachs and having tended to their personal needs, the girls felt revived and sat with Bill in the open doorway. The train dragged slowly out of the yard, and as the countryside passed by the old man spun stories of his travels and adventures. He never spoke of his life before becoming a hobo, never gave a hint if he ever had a wife or children. If he ever had a family, his granddaughters would probably be about the age of the runaway girls.

"I'll be a hobo until I can't tramp no more," Bill said. "Then I'll find some nice place away from the rest of the world, preferably a warm climate, settle there and live out my remaining days in peace and contentment."

At midday Bill opened his big canvas tote and produced two loaves of bread and a gallon of milk. He told the girls, "Help yourself. Tear off a hunk of bread and wash it down with milk." He also shared a sack of apples. For dessert he opened a can of stewed tomatoes with his pocketknife and passed it around. The girls took turns spearing tomatoes with the knife and slurping them.

The canvas bag turned out to be a cornucopia of treats. No sooner had they finished eating, than Bill returned to the bag and pulled out items of clothing. He handed a pair of trousers, a work shirt and a pair of heavy, well-oiled boots to Zelda, along with a warning, "The road's a dangerous place. Best if you didn't look so much like a dame." He tossed several changes of clothes and a felt hat to Red and said, "Tuck your hair up in this." He glanced at Bertie and advised her, "Wear this here shirt over the outside of your overalls."

"What do we owe you?" Bertie wanted to know.

"Pleasure's all mine," he said, flashing his near-toothless grin. He gave the girls more clothing and even totes so they could store their newfound treasures. Bill continued to sit in the doorway, basking in the warmth that comes from sharing, while the girls remained unsure of his motives and collectively wondered why he had fed and clothed them. It was Zelda who felt compelled to ask, "Why'd you go do it?"

"Do what?"

"Share your food. Give us things?"

"Cause you needed it, and I wanted to."

"You got kids?" asked Bertie.

"Maybe I do. Maybe I don't." He became pensive. "I had a woman one time in my life. Nothing I did ever satisfied her. If I got turkey she wanted ham. If I got jelly she wanted jam. One day it hit me that I'd be better off without her. And that was the day I done hit the road.

"I get along fine. If a man don't have a woman, don't have a home, he can live on the cheap. Figure it this way, lot of things can kill a body and I want to make sure what kills me ain't hard work. Only time I work is when I need something. It takes money to eat. Takes money to drink. I don't drink that much anymore.

"You gals go down the road and you're gonna learn about bums. Most men wind up out here 'cause of a woman. Either they had a gal, but couldn't hang onto her, or they wanted one and never got her. Usually something 'bout like that.

"Anyways, I've smelled pine trees in Oregon, salt air in the Florida Keys, ate taffy in Nova Scotia and beans in old Mexico. Hell, back when I smoked I was known to double back on a place on account of the size of the butts I found in the gutter. I've lay dead-to-the-world in flophouses where no one cared enough to check on me until the rent came due. Walked many a mile in wet shoes and had the leather turn hard as iron. Been caught in the snow without so much as a blanket. In my travels I've seen it all; done it all."

He dug around in his tote and produced a bent and creased photograph. He held it so the girls could see. "This here's my only regret. Yeah, I got a kid, a boy. Never seen him after the day I took off. Today be his 41st birthday. Probably wouldn't want nothin' to do with his old man; some damn hobo, knight of the road, down-and-outer." With that said, Bill put the photograph away and said, "I've talked enough."

Red lay back against the wall of the boxcar and soon drifted to sleep. When she woke up, Bill was sitting cross-legged in front of the open door whittling on a chunk of pine with his pocketknife. Several times he paused to examine his work. Not satisfied, he went back to whittling. When, in his estimation, his carving was flawless he pitched it away, out the door, gathered all the little curly shavings he had made and stuffed them in his coat pocket. They would be kindling for his next fire.

Red moved near the opening and took a seat beside Bill. He did the bulk of the talking. The gist of what he had to say was that luxury was spoiling people in the modern world. One example he used was folks now expected to have ice for their drinks, not as a treat on Sunday as used to be the case, but every day of the week. His point was that any indulgence, when enjoyed on a regular basis, soon becomes a necessity.

"If you could only have one thing in the world what would it be?" Red asked.

Bill was quick to answer. "Freedom. Got freedom, got it all. Don't have to worry about material possessions. Don't have to worry about responsibility. I got no more responsibility than a one-eyed jackrabbit. And you know something? If you're truly free, you never have to grow up. All you got to do is grow old. And I've done a pretty fair job of that." He laughed at himself.

Bill rambled over the countryside without ever having a destination in mind. He said he might continue northwest to

155

Seattle, or just as easily he could catch a train for Galveston, Sioux City or San Diego. If he had any plans at all, they were subject to change. Nearing Pocatello he told the girls he was dropping off. One by one they gave him a hug and wished him well. They said they would miss him and thanked him for his generosity, sage advice and friendliness. He pushed away from the train, took a couple halting steps and turned to face the girls. He gave a snappy salute, turned and walked back up the tracks.

⊢⊣⊢⊣⊢⊣⊢⊣

The freight continued south to Utah. Approaching the Ogden yards the train slowed, and when it was safe the three girls dropped off and ducked into the willows. They had made a pact to find work in Ogden and once they had saved some money they planned to continue on together to California.

"I'm dying to get out of this monkey suit," Zelda said. She leaned against a boulder and removed her boots. She replaced her trousers and shirt, all gifts from Railroad Bill, with the dress and saddle shoes she had kept tightly rolled to protect them from the soot and dust. She ran her long fingers through her short black hair, shook her head and announced, "There, I guess I'm presentable."

Bertie teased, "I don't know...maybe a little soap and water might help."

"I'm trying to overlook that," Zelda said. "Truth is, I'd kill for a hot bath. Not necessarily even a bubble bath, nothing that fancy, just a whole lotta hot water in a tub deep enough to drown in. I'd soak until my skin falls off."

The girls walked toward town. Near the outskirts, they came across a traveling carnival. Performers were busy setting up tents in a cow pasture. Before the hour was out, Red had a job setting up portable outhouses, Bertie was busy memorizing the barker's spiel for the two-headed calf exhibit, and Zelda had wormed her way into an acting career. She was hired as the latest vamp, in a long string of vamps, for the slightly naughty *Girl in the Bed* routine.

The *Girl in the Bed* act was held inside the privacy of a small tent and required a scantily clad girl to recline across a bed that was set on a platform above the heads of the onlookers. Participants traded tickets they purchased for baseballs. The balls were thrown at a target. If the target was hit, the near side of the bed tripped, dropped down and unceremoniously tossed the girl onto the mattress at eyelevel to the crowd of onlookers.

"You'll wear this," the carnival woman told Zelda, holding a pair of red panties, matching bra and sexy negligee.

"I couldn't wear such a flimsy thing in public. I don't want to be arrested for indecent exposure."

"That has been taken care of. There will be no arrests. I promise."

"Can I wear a bathing suit?"

The woman shook her head. "If you don't want the job, there are plenty of other girls who do. Make up your mind, sweetie."

"Can I wear my own panties underneath? I'd feel better."

"Long as they don't show. Now we need to get you prettied up."

The carnival woman led the way to an outdoor shower, protected on three sides by a canvas cover. She watched as Zelda removed her clothes and was pleasantly surprised to see she was rather big-breasted for such a thin, narrow-shouldered girl. Her hips were round and her behind was nicely curved and firm. Her backbone made the carnival lady recall a beach in California where she stood and watched scrawny-backed little girls building sand castles and getting sunburned. She instinctively knew this new *Girl in the Bed* was going to make her a lot of money.

Zelda scraped and scoured, buffed and washed and all the while lukewarm water cascaded over her from a rusty overhead pipe. When the woman finally turned off the water, Zelda accepted the offered towel, and after blotting her hair she wrapped the towel around herself and followed the woman to the tent.

Before long, her short black hair was wrapped in curlers, makeup had been applied, cheeks powdered and rouged, lips revived with a lush application of red lipstick, eyebrows plucked and highlighted, fingernails and toenails cleaned and painted a shade of red to match the lipstick. Toward the end of the session, while her hair was being combed, she was feeling pleasantly pampered.

As the carnival opening drew near, the woman climbed the stairs to the bed and assumed a position on her side, sheet draped over her lower half, head propped on an elbow. "This is how I want you."

Zelda traded places and struck an alluring pose. The carnival woman was impressed. Under the artificial lighting, Zelda was absolutely radiant, and as glamorous and seductive as a movie star.

"One final touch." The woman handed Zelda a black headband. "Put it on."

The show began with Zelda lying on the bed, partially draped with the sheet, wearing the red bra, double panties, abbreviated negligee and the headband. The first customer arrived, followed by more men who gawked, paid their money and pitched baseballs. A freckle-faced boy was the first to hit the target. The mechanism on the bed released, and Zelda tumbled onto the mattress. But even in falling, and climbing the stairs to the bed, she proved to be a talented temptress, giving flirtatious peeks at her private treasures and always holding out promise of even more the next time the target was hit. While the men lusted, she coyly batted her eyes and pouted her lips. Every man with a dime in his pocket wanted in on the action.

Zelda found it advantageous to talk to the throwers. She made her voice husky as she chided them, "What you got, Big Boy?" and "Wanna see more?" and "I'm all yours. Just hit the target, handsome."

The carnival woman was not sure whether Zelda was a born Jezebel or just a damn convincing actress, deciding she was a touch of both. The following day, when the carnival pulled out heading to Cortez, Colorado, Zelda was riding in the back seat of a four-passenger Cadillac sport Phaeton. She had been given her own trailer to live in and promised 10 percent of the nightly take. Already her likeness was being printed on handbills that would be distributed to workingmen from Dove Creek to Durango. She was the new star of the traveling show.

Bertie didn't know why the carnival hadn't hired her to go on the road, too. She thought she had done a good job as a barker, standing in front of the two-headed calf exhibit, calling to curious onlookers, "Ladies and gentlemen. Step right up. See this absolute freak of nature. You will brag to your friends and neighbors. It's educational. It's *SENSATIONAL!* One thin dime. See the wondrous two-headed calf. Step right up. How about you, young man? Do you want to be the first?"

The young man was a shill and over and over again he lead a fresh group of curious viewers into the tent. After a moment, disappointment written across their faces upon having witnessed the fetus of a two-headed calf stuffed into a gallon jug filled with formaldehyde, they filed out the back flap grumbling that what they had seen was not even remotely similar to the artist's rendition on the poster in front of the tent.

During the evening, a man wearing a cowboy hat hung around the fringe of the crowd near the two-headed calf tent. He took a tin of Velvet tobacco, and a slender rolling paper, and built lazy cigarettes; packing them just so, moistening the paper with a series of little flicks from his tongue. He retrieved wooden matches from his pocket, lifted a leg and stuck the matches on his trousers. As the matches flared, he lit his cigarettes.

When Bertie went on break the fellow followed her, and Bertie, as edgy as a cat in an electrical storm, walked up to the cowboy and asked, "You spyin' on me, mister?"

The man squinted through the smoke, gave her a thin-lipped smile and drawled, "Kinda hate to admit it, but you're about the prettiest dang filly I ever done laid eyes on. I've been waitin' fer a chance to introduce myself. Name's Carson Lang." He touched the brim of his black hat with a forefinger, and tipped the hat back slightly.

Bertie never stopped to consider how odd it was that some men instinctively know which women they can approach. Carson took a last casual drag off his cigarette and discarded it with a practiced flick of his forefinger and all she knew for certain was this man needed her, and she needed this man.

Now as she stood with Red on the shoulder of the road watching the carnival pull out of town, Carson showed up in his pickup truck. He pulled near the girls and stopped, leaned over, threw open the passenger door and was looking straight at Bertie when he said, "Got me a job in Nevada breaking wild mustangs. Wanna go along for the ride, babe?"

Bertie licked an index finger and raised it in the air. Another time she might have been testing the velocity or direction of the wind, but this time she said, "Whichever way the wind blows me."

She slid onto the seat, right next to Carson. The last Red saw of them, Bertie had her head resting on the cowboy's scrawny shoulder. After that, Red was alone.

Chapter Ten

Jack stood on a small rise overlooking Spring Valley, California, drinking in the mad profusion of colors: the dazzling yellow ball of afternoon sun, the sparkling blue of the Pacific Ocean and the checkerboard of green and golden fields. He thought about the long journey that had ultimately brought him to California, and some about his friend, Kelsey Conger. Jack knew he had seen the last of Kelsey.

"Kelsey, you poor son of a bitch. You gave up too soon."

At that moment, a half-continent away, a jobless anarchist materialized from a crowd, thrust the barrel of a revolver forward and shouted, "Too many people are starving to death. He pulled the trigger. The bullet missed President-elect Franklin Delano Roosevelt by a fraction of an inch, but killed the man FDR was standing with, Anton Cermak, the mayor of Chicago.

If Jack had known about the incident in Chicago he would have empathized with the would-be assassin. He knew how challenging it could be when a decent, hard-working man was denied employment. He understood how a person, provoked by hopelessness and depression, could be driven to lash out and do things not normally in his nature. In his estimation, it was the personal greed of business tycoons, and the incompetence of the government and its elected officials, that was the root cause of the Great Depression and the unraveling of the nation's social fabric.

He spent the remainder of that day, and many more days searching for employment, finding nothing more than an occasional day job. As a last resort, he willingly became a pawn of the politics he condemned and despised. He joined the Civilian Conservation Corps, a federal agency instituted as a part of FDR's progressive New Deal reform package to combat the Great Depression and put unemployed young men to work on reclamation and conservation projects in rural areas. Pay was room, board, and thirty bucks a month.

Jack was sent to the CCC camp in the Vallecito Mountains east of San Diego, where the desert terrain was populated with a profusion of uninteresting rocks, spiky cactus, and twisted Ocotillo plants with whip-like branches. He was assigned to a two-man canvas tent and his bunkmate was a 24-year-old black man who told Jack when they met, "I go by Turk."

Turk, plucked fresh off the streets of Seattle, stood six feet tall and wore tight-fitting T-shirts that showed off his well-muscled physique. He proclaimed he had boxed a little, mined for gold in Alaska, felled timber in the Queen Charlotte Islands of Canada, fished commercially for salmon and tuna, and raced motorcycles professionally.

Jack's initial impression was that his bunkmate was a blowhard who had a story for every occasion. But that changed the day Turk took Jack to a gold claim he had filed on. He showed how to pan for gold. On his very first pan, Jack discovered fine yellow dust suspended in a layer of black sand, and a nugget the size of a small pencil eraser. He was instantly hooked. What excited him most was not the weight of the nugget he held in the palm of his hand, nor its monetary value, but the possibilities and potential it represented. Nevermore, when times were tough, would he be without a paying job. He told himself he could always scratch the bosom of Mother Earth and find something of value.

During the day, they worked for the CCC cutting trails into the hillsides. After work, while the others lazed around writing sentimental letters home or slipped off to take a dip in the swimming hole, the two hiked to the pocket of placer gold. They worked shoulder-to-shoulder, shirts off, shoveling sand and gravel into a small sluice box fed by water from a small mountain stream. The steady work soon was good for Jack, tempering his muscles, making him strong and giving him endurance.

Returning to the camp one evening, he saw a makeshift prize-fighting ring had been strung between four trees. A pair of fighters were sparring and Jack inquired what was going on. He was told, "Come Saturday they're having a smoker in Descanso. We have to pick representatives from the camp in three weight divisions. How about you? Wanna shot at lightweight?"

"Yeah, sure. Hell, I'll give it a try."

Turk had listened to Jack tell stories of his fighting days, and what impressed him now was Jack's willingness to get in the ring. What he did not know was, with only one good leg, if Jack could handle himself in the ring. He pulled Jack aside.

"Don't you think you should knock a little of the rust off before you commit yourself? What say, you and me spar a couple rounds?"

When their turn came, the two strapped on the gloves. A wooden spoon banged against the bottom of a pan and Jack came out quickly, shuffling forward, favoring his bad leg. From his many previous fights, he knew that in those first few seconds most fighters are not yet resigned to the brutalities of the ring. One good punch might melt their resolve the same way a chunk of ice swiftly thaws in the heat of the noonday sun.

He faked a lazy left jab and delivered a sneaky overhead right that landed flush on Turk's left ear and sent the bigger man reeling backwards under the impact.

"Hey, we're friends. This is supposed to be a fun sparring session."

Jack dropped his gloves to his side and bounced back and forth from his good leg to his bad, grinning. "Want me to take it easy on you?"

"Hell no. Come on, let's see what you got." Turk motioned with his gloves for Jack to move forward.

With his awkward gait, Jack circled one way and then the other, finding an opening and unleashing a flurry of deceptively fast combinations. Turk absorbed what he could, but when the punishment threatened to overwhelm him he took a stumbling step backwards and cried out, "You win!"

Jack started to relax. That was when Turk threw a blindside punch, the meat of the glove catching Jack on the left temple and provoking a series of rapid responses. He bent at the waist, staggered to one side and drew a succession of quick, shallow breaths. He gathered himself, feinted one way, moved the other, and like the short strokes of a piston firing within the confines of a cylinder, he drove his fists into Turk's exposed belly. Each punch was delivered with lightning speed and deadly accuracy.

When Turk's hands came together to try to protect his stomach and ribs, Jack moved upstairs. A sharp right caught Turk on the point of his chin. He fell backwards and his feet, unable or unwilling to keep up with his momentum, went rubbery. He plopped down unceremoniously on the seat of his trousers.

"Get up you son of a bitch!"

Turk shook his head. "No way. I ain't agonna fight no more. Not you. Never again."

Turk had acquired a newfound respect for his friend and now saw Jack as a boxer with speed and power and a warrior's instincts to finish the kill. As they walked away from the ring, he offered to train Jack.

"With your talents and me in your corner, I think we can make a hell of a professional career out of it."

Jack easily won the right to represent the camp at the smoker in the nearby town of Descanso, where he was pitted against the local lightweight champion. The fight was not much of a contest. Jack knocked out his opponent in the first minute. For his efforts he was awarded a dollar six bits and a chocolate cake baked by the Descanso Women's Club. The boys from camp made short work of the cake.

<hr />

When their six-month CCC stint was over, Jack and Turk drew their paychecks, sold the gold they had recovered, and moved to San Diego. They found a room to rent near the Main Street Gym. The gym, a boxing outpost in an impoverished section of the city, was dark and reeked of human sweat. Faded and torn fight posters made the walls look dingy. Sounds, guttural and savage, echoed around the open room: the sharp slap of leather gloves against heavy canvas bags, the rat-tat-tat of the speed bags, and grunts, groans and bellows from fighters sparring in the elevated ring.

Some of the top names in the fight game trained at Main Street Gym. Jack was there every day and soon became a regular sparring partner for Sweet Candy Anderson, a legitimate top ten middleweight contender. Sweet Candy used Jack to improve his hand speed, vigorously working to catch up to and hit a smaller, quicker man.

To the other fighters, Jack was considered a bit of a novelty. To hide his prosthesis he refused to fight in shorts and always wore trousers. If someone had seen him before his accident, and compared him to the fighter he had become, they would recognize the quickness of his hands and his punching power. The big difference was, before he had moved with a cat-like gracefulness, but now his movements were coarse, herky-jerky, almost clumsy. To compensate for his limitations, he had become more of a defensive fighter and a cool and calculating counter-puncher. Rather than moving straight ahead, he moved side-to-side as hypnotically as a swaying cobra. When he struck it was rarely with a single punch, most often a flurry of well-conceived and effectively delivered combinations.

Word of his pugilistic prowess made the rounds, and when an amateur fighter on an undercard was injured in an automobile accident, Jack was the only man who would agree to take the fight on a single day's notice. He won by TKO when his opponent's corner refused to allow their bloodied fighter to answer the bell for the third. Turk parlayed that victory into a scheduled hundred-dollar fight in Long Beach. It was the big break Jack had been waiting for—his professional debut—and he anticipated this fight would start him on the road leading to the World Championship.

He stepped up his training; running and jumping rope. He performed a thousand push-ups, a thousand sit-ups and a hundred pull-ups every day. He worked on the heavy bag, the light bag and sparred three times a week. He honed his boxing skills and at the end of the six weeks he was as ready as any fighter could hope to be.

Maximillion Baer, better known as Max—in 1934 he would become the Heavyweight Champion of the World—was an up-and-comer and a regular at the Main Street Gym. Big Max was a playboy. He was flashy and loved to laugh and drink, and party. His lighthearted style carried over into the ring where he was often more of an entertainer than a boxer. At Main Street Gym he made wisecracks to his sparring partners and joked with ringsiders. He had all the talent in the world, but despised the work. He chose to hang around and simply go through the motions of training. It was odd—they seemed to be such polar opposites in size and work ethic—but Max took a liking to Jack and they struck up a friendship. It was amusing to see the small fighter and the big fighter together; shy Jack and flamboyant Max, the serious one and the fun-loving one.

Max was blessed with one of the most striking physical builds ever seen in the ring. He had tremendously wide shoulders, barrel chest and a chiseled waistline. He was a country boy, reared on a ranch near Livermore, California. He quit school as a teenager and took a job in the slaughterhouse owned by his father. Max worked on the kill floor, swinging a 10-pound sledgehammer. It was this repetitive action that developed the long, supple arm and shoulder muscles that gave him his sensational hitting power.

At age 19, Max had thrown a punch at a cowboy in a Livermore dance hall and the cowboy dropped like he had been shot. This gave Max a grand idea. He bought a pair of boxing gloves and within a year he was, without ever bothering to learn the fundamentals of the sweet science or even the subtle aspects of self-defense, fighting professionally.

Max had the rare ability of being able to take a punch, and was perfectly willing to put himself in jeopardy in order to be in position to land his big punch, a deadly right. Deadly it was. Max would later kill two men with that punch: Frank Campbell in San Francisco and Ernie Schaaf, who suffered a brain hemorrhage and died soon after the fight.

On the night of Jack's first professional fight, Max, along with two women from his stable of girlfriends, drove to the fight. He was there to have fun. It was an excuse for another night on the town. He and his girls were shown to ringside seats. When Jack crawled between the ropes and into the ring, Max was on his feet enthusiastically cheering and pounding his massive hands together.

"There's our man. Show 'em what you got, mighty Jack."

Jack opened his long robe. He was wearing trousers. The referee came to his corner and informed him, "If you fight professionally, you wear trunks. You've gotta have trunks."

Turk protested, but to no avail and Jack was forced to return to his dressing room. The crowd booed the delay. When he reentered the ring and opened his robe, exposing his prosthesis, the booing ended abruptly and the crowd drew a collective gasp. His opponent shouted to the referee, "I ain't fightin' no goddamned cripple."

The referee announced that, according to the rules of the California Boxing Commission, a one-legged fighter was not allowed to compete in a professional fight. Max, infuriated at the decision, threw a chair into the ring. He bellowed that, one-legged or two-legged, Jack was the best fighter, pound-for-pound, on the planet. But his gesticulations were to no avail and Jack's professional career ended before it ever began. Without hope of orchestrating Jack's professional career, Turk lost interest in the fight game and drifted back to his old haunts in Seattle.

With no reason to remain in San Diego, Jack left town, catching a ride with a salesman in a Pontiac who drove him as far as Yuma, Arizona. Here, where the highway bisected the Southern Pacific mainline, he caught a freight train to

Phoenix, sharing a boxcar with a group of men who were out of work, broke, weary and disheartened.

In Phoenix he was lucky and caught on as a short order cook at the Lucky Miner Diner. But the heat of the grill, and having to constantly be on his feet, rubbed Jack's stump raw. It was so tender and painful he was forced to quit.

He limped to the rail yard and caught a ride on an eastbound freight. In the boxcar he found a discarded tabloid newspaper, and to occupy his time, he read the news of the rich and famous, the star-crossed darlings of the *Cafe Society*.

"Seven-year-old Lucy Cotton Thomas appeared in court today to demand a higher allowance from the estate of her father...Her mother insisted that the existing allowance was wholly inadequate since it restricts expenditures to $800 per month as the child's share of the rent of a Fifth Avenue apartment, $350 for chauffeur and maid service, $300 for clothing, $600 for food, $700 for furnishings and repairs, and only $400 for dancing lessons, music, flowers, etc..."

Another article announced that Woolworth heiress Barbara Hutton had received $45 million on her 21st birthday. An unrelated story mentioned, because of the ongoing Depression, the pay of Woolworth salesgirls had been reduced by a dollar a week. Also in the news was an article about another young heiress, Doris Duke. She inherited $30 million, along with homes in four states and a fifth in the Antibes, all fully staffed with servants. He read about families—the Astors, Vanderbilts, Mellons—and children who received the greatest rewards imaginable by doing absolutely nothing to achieve them. To a young man like Jack, barely getting by in life, such news was demoralizing, and in disgust he tossed the newspaper from the speeding train.

Nearing El Paso, he waited for the train to slow before dropping to the ground. The night was big and cold and low clouds spit rain. He made his way toward the lights of a pool hall, pushed open the door, went inside and took a seat at the bar. Prohibition had been repealed and once again alcohol was being openly served. When the bartender came around and asked what he could get him, Jack replied, "Beer."

While he waited, he tried to take a deep breath to cleanse his lungs of the grit and smoke of the train. The smell of cigars and cigarettes hung as heavy as engine oil in the room. He moaned under the dull, constant pain of his leg. If the leg was gone why in hell did it continue to hurt? He did not know. He just knew it did.

Jack accepted that he was no better off than an ordinary tramp. Failure drove them all: losing a job, losing a farm, losing a woman. Failures added up to nights in boxcars, in the rain, waking up in alleys, on thin mattresses at some nameless mission, watching green neon flicker and flash *JESUS SAVES*, listening to crazy alcoholics crying and screaming, Christmases spent at a Salvation Army with a bunch of well-intentioned volunteers who doled out servings of cold turkey and mashed potatoes with lumpy gravy. All he had to look forward to was an endless string of odd jobs, handouts and more rides to nowhere. His life, like all the others who were in his same predicament, would be ugly, pointless and wasted. Yesterday would be the same as today. Today the same as tomorrow; days spent drifting on sameness.

He drank his beer and watched a moth batter itself senseless against a bare bulb. A toothless old drunk was telling a story about a dog he once owned that swallowed a shotgun shell. "Took him to the vet an' he says to force a bottle of castor oil down him, and be sure and not point his ass end at anyone." Drunken laugher. More beer. From the jukebox came a soft rain of melancholy music, the sadly romantic notes seeped into all the desolate corners of the room. Dawn would soon arrive dragging with it a veneer of dew, and a low, white mist forming on the ground would hang around until the sun burned it away. Another day. More disappointment. More failure. Sameness.

"Can I get another?"

The beer arrived and the amber liquid seemed to broaden Jack's night, giving it a grander dimension than it deserved. Alcohol masked his pain, disappointments, frustrations. Alcohol stirred and provoked him. He stared hard into the bottom of his nearly empty glass, as if searching for a big idea. Instead, an imperceptible panic grabbed hold of him and caused his mind to snap. He abruptly swung from his stool. With one hand jammed in his coat pocket, making it seem as though the pocket held a gun, he barked orders as patrons scattered.

"Do what I say! Line up against the wall! Over there." He jerked his head toward the near wall and addressed the bartender. "Empty the till! Give me the money! Move it!"

Jack knew precisely what he was doing—he was the man in charge, the one who commanded absolute power—and yet he was also aware of an odd sensation, as if he was merely a bystander, an observer, and therefore blameless for his own actions. The bartender placed a fistful of paper bills onto the bar. Jack scooped them up and shoved them in his coat pocket.

"Who's got a rig?" Again Jack made a threatening motion, this time addressing one man in particular. "You got one?" The man shook his head up and down. "Give me the key! Give me the goddamn key!" The man handed over a key. "Which one is it?"

"Th...th...the Ford by the door. But that's my only transportation. I've gotta have it."

"Shut up! Don't nobody try and be a hero." Jack reached blindly for the door, opened it and stepped into the broad desert night where a cool wind slapped his sweat-splashed face and woke him to what he had done. As he opened the door of the Ford and crawled behind the wheel, it occurred to him that maybe, if he could go back in time, he could undo all of this and just wipe the slate clean. But he could not. He would have to live with the consequences of his actions. He inserted the key in the ignition, his foot found the starter, the Ford cranked over. The engine sprang to life. Wheels spun. Gravel pinged off the underside, ricocheting against the metal as Jack—now a holdup man and fugitive from the law—made good his escape.

He drove the stolen Ford across the Mexican border and sold it to a restaurant owner in the town of Torreon, getting a meal and $50 American money to boot. Then wanting to put more distance between himself and the scene of his crime, he caught a succession of rides: automobiles, buses, trucks, a wagon pulled by mules and even a donkey-drawn cart. It was not until he reached the Gulf of Mexico, insulated by a thousand miles from the legal arm of the United States, that he began to feel safe.

He settled in the seaboard town of Tampico. One day, while lounging in a cantina, he was approached by a man who introduced himself as Marcias Rodriguez. He professed to be a Mexican national, born in the United States, and boasted of serving in the U.S. Army and being a well-known soldier of fortune. His current occupation, he claimed, was transporting bananas downriver from a jungle plantation to a harbor where they were loaded on ocean-going ships.

"I do not trust my own people. They steal from me."

"What makes you think that?"

"I know. That is why I want to hire you to go to the plantation and find out how they do it. Do they steal my bananas in the field or on the river? I pay you $10 a day. Work with them, side-by-side in the fields. Keep your eyes and ears open. You learn. You tell me."

"Ten bucks a day?"

Marcias nodded.

"For Christ's sake, that's more than I've ever made in any day of my entire life, except for boxing."

"You a professional fighter? Even better."

"Not professionally, but I've fought for money lots of times."

Marcias made sure he was not being watched, cautiously removed a small pistol from his pocket and passed it under the table to Jack. "Maybe you need this," he said.

Jack lowered an eyebrow. "Is it that dangerous?" Not waiting for an answer, he accepted the weapon, cautiously tucking it in the waistband under his shirt.

"Don't wave it around. They kill you for a gun."

Chapter Eleven

The plantation, located 20 miles up the Panuco River, had been carved from the jungle and then was planted to banana trees. Jack caught passage on one of the empty banana scows. Upon reaching the plantation he was assigned to the cavy crew, herding in lightweight workhorses and putting them in harness. The horses pulled banana-laden wagons from the fields to the dock. The horses were changed after every other trip.

He lived among the Mexican workers, slept in the bunkhouse and ate in the cookhouse. The Mexicans were a suspicious lot and gave him a wide berth, all except a young girl named Lupie. She was a light-skinned Veracruz Indian who helped with the cooking chores. The first time she spoke to Jack, she shyly asked in broken English, "You want lay with me?"

"I have only 75 centavos."

She said that would be enough and told him where they should meet. After that encounter, they met often, and sometimes she refused to take his money.

He thought their meetings were secret, but one afternoon as he was bringing in fresh horses, a group of men appeared at the corral gate waving their arms and refusing to allow the horses to pass. Jack yelled, "Get the hell out of my way!"

A Mexican man stepped forward and made a threatening move by pulling free the machete he wore in a scabbard on his belt. Jack had seen these natives swing machetes, cutting arm-sized hardwood limbs with a single slice, and knew full well the damage a machete could do. He took a step back, lost his footing on the uneven ground, tripped and fell.

The Mexican flailed his machete in a circle over his head and brought it down in a powerful and deadly arc. Just before impact, Jack rolled to one side and watched the polished silver blade bite into the black soil. He reacted by reaching under his shirt, pulling free the pistol and pointing it at his attacker. He fully expected the man to step away, but he did not. When he began to raise the machete once again, Jack's finger curled around the trigger. The bullet struck the Mexican in the belly, making a thud like a sharp ax driven into punky wood. The man's eyes widened. He took a halting half-step backward, dropped the machete and clutched at his stomach. His legs gave out and he toppled onto the ground, lying there on his back, motionless, blood oozing from his wound and staining his white shirt.

Lupie came running from the cook shack. She swept the man up into her arms, tears stained her brown cheeks. She spoke to Jack like the foreman of a jury reading a guilty verdict. "You kill him."

"He came at me with his machete." Jack looked toward the others for confirmation, but those who had witnessed the attack and shooting were moving away and disappearing into the jungle. He made a frantic gesture, an all-encompassing sweep of his hand. "They saw…it was self-defense."

"He my husband. You go! They kill you."

Jack ran to the dock and stowed away on a boat preparing to leave for downriver. Upon reaching Tampico, Jack told Marcias the details of the shooting. Marcias seemed very concerned. "Give me the gun. We get you away from here."

Jack was taken by ship around the Yucatan Peninsula and put ashore at Panama City. He proceeded directly to the nearest bar to have a drink. He had not even had time to be served when a brawl broke out. Even though he was not involved in the fight, when the police arrived they arrested Jack and took him to an ancient jail chiseled into a cliff on a solid rock wall. The cave-like cells were barred in the front and overlooked the tranquil Caribbean Sea. At the back of each cell ran a small stream of water in a wooden trough. It served two dissimilar purposes, as a water source as well as the latrine.

Jack held tightly to the bars, squinting at the flat glare of pale sunlight filtered through heavy gray clouds. Gulls screamed and wheeled along the edge of the cliff. The air was foul and seemed thin, empty, lifeless.

On the second day of his confinement, a man came around carrying a big black pot. He scooped soup with a ladle, reached through the bars and dumped it in the battered metal cup Jack held firmly with both hands. Jack had to pick out the maggots floating on the surface and fought the black flies that buzzed around trying to steal whatever they could get. Later, a grimy fog moved in and held as tight as a drab blanket spread over the world.

A guard emerged from out of this gloom, accompanied by a man dressed in a tailored blue suit. They stopped in front of Jack's cell, and with a jangle of keys the jailer opened the door. The man wearing the suit told Jack, "Come."

He obediently followed the men down the narrow walkway while prisoners, acting as wild as caged animals, shouted obscenities at their passing and made a bewildering racket by running metal cups back and forth over the metal bars.

Jack was taken to the wharf where a United Fruit steamship was tied to the dock, and ordered to board the ship. As he started up the gangplank, the man wearing the suit told him, "You lucky man. American consulate make arrangement for you have passage to New Orleans. You not welcome no more again in Panama."

When the ship landed in New Orleans, Jack walked through the streets and breathed in the rich aromas of spicy Cajun cooking, but he had no money to buy food and on an empty stomach he hiked to the rail yard where he planned to hop a freight train. While in prison he had formulated a plan, promising when he was released, he'd head straight to California and hunt gold.

The Great Depression still devasted the rural south, and he joined a horde of nomadic tramps gathered to hitch a free ride on the train. These men were vainly hoping a change in geography would improve their likelihood of finding employment, but the railroad was taking an active stance to stop them. A small army of vigilant detectives stood guard over the train as it readied to depart.

Railroad dicks—nightsticks flailing and pistols drawn—swept the train. They pulled bums from cars and hiding spots, even where they clung to the rods under the carriage. Bums were pushed, prodded, kicked and clubbed. Jack watched and waited until the train began to move, allowing it to pick up speed, and then on his gimpy leg he rushed forward. He made a determined stab at a ladder, grabbed it tightly and allowed the forward momentum of the train to sweep him off his feet. A burst of blue, and a telltale ZING very near his head let him know shots were being fired. This propelled him to swing his good leg onto the ladder and scramble up and into the empty scrap metal car.

Long moments passed, and as he regained his normal breathing, he once again felt the familiar sway of the car and heard the hypnotizing cadence of wheels passing over breaks in the rails. The night sky was lighter than the dense foliage overhanging the rails. Time and miles seemed to melt into the same unit of measurement. The moon, as soft and vibrant as a delicate yellow rose unfolding, began to emerge and reflected across the slick black waters of a bayou. Fireflies flitted about, mixing their pinpoints of light with sparks escaping from the smokestack of the locomotive.

One moment Jack was drinking in all the fabulous sights and sounds and smells of the hot, humid night, and then he felt a strange sensation and instinctively knew his world was not right. His first impulse was that of guilt—the robbery he committed in El Paso, the killing in Mexico—but with astonishing swiftness the sickness that was inside him, most likely caused from a mosquito bite in Panama City, prevailed over everything. A ragged bolt of hot lightning flashed between Jack's temples, pulsating and intensifying with each beat of his heart. Beads of sweat popped out on his forehead and he began to shiver and shake. In his belly, a sharp stab of excruciating pain forced him to double over. He fell heavily to the bottom of the empty rail car. An involuntary reaction triggered his knees to come to his chest in a fetal position. His stomach convulsed. He choked, gagged, coughed and vomited. Shortly after that, mercifully, he lost consciousness.

It was still dark when he woke up to excruciating pain. It was only with a supreme effort that he was able to haul his battered body upright and into a sitting position. His shirt was drenched in sweat and vile, sticky vomit. He unbuttoned the shirt, tossed it aside and then struggled to stand. When he finally gained his feet he looked over the edge and discovered his rail car, along with several others, had been abandoned on a siding. From a nearby swamp came a bizarre commotion: deep-throated bellows of bullfrogs, high-pitched whines of insects, rustling leaves, fluttering wings, splashing water. Each little noise was like another blood vessel exploding in his brain. This confused him all the more. He was unsure how long he had been unconscious, where he might be, or how far it was to the nearest town. He knew he needed help and forced his aching muscles to respond. He clambered over the edge of the rail car and awkwardly slid down the ladder to the ground. His prosthesis was twisted at an odd angle. He tugged at the straps to straighten it, and then began walking in a lurching, uncertain, wobbly gait. He was aware enough of his surroundings to know grave danger dogged his every step. There were alligators, water moccasins and coral snakes. He was cold, then hot, and hot and cold at the same time. His reserve of strength was failing fast and yet he continued shuffling woodenly from one tie to the next. His muscles twitched, began to spasm and cramp. Fever burned. Chills made his teeth chatter.

He was nearing exhaustion and began looking for a place to lie down. He had the presence of mind to know if he fell asleep on the tracks, a passing train would surely cut him in half. He found a flat spot, dropped down into a fetal position and immediately fell into a deep sleep that washed away his pain. During the darkness of night a fog, as tenuous as a soft whisper, crept from where it hovered over the water, made its way to the land, and gathered around brittle tree branches the way wool sticks to the bottom strand of barbed wire. An emerging sun burned the fog away. When Jack did wake up, his eyes were nearly swollen shut, his lips enlarged and discolored, and the skin on his upper body had turned an unnatural yellow. He was shirtless and covered with bumps and welts from the gnawing of blood-sucking insects. His throat was parched and he ached all over. His head pounded and fever burned. But more than anything he was mad with an irrational desire to scratch his chest, belly and back, where the bugs had been at work. He rose from the muddy ground and began moving forward. He could not resist and clawed his skin until it bled. He stumbled along an endless row of railroad ties, only to discover the ties had been replaced by a plank boardwalk. He was fighting to rationalize how this could possibly have come to pass when his legs quit working and he fell, landing face down in front of the entrance to a store. He was aware of nothing more.

The widow woman who owned the store found him. She stepped around his body—covered with bites, blood, mud and vomit—and called the doctor. When the doctor arrived, he examined the bacon-rind-thin young man and recognized the telltale signs of a tropical disease. He ordered ice packed around his patient to bring down his fever, and directed he be transported to the hospital just over the state line in Beaumont, Texas. Here Jack was diagnosed, as the doctor had suspected, with acute malaria.

In fighting the infectious disease, Jack faced an adversary so formidable that his own strength and will to live were almost irrelevant. While in a state of near-coma he experienced wild hallucinations, seeing people he knew or had only read about. They appeared lifelike, as if they were actually in his room. Will Rogers spoke to him. Babe Ruth swung a broom and hit a home run. A crowd of cheering fans stood on the ceiling. The walls breathed in and out with billowing cheeks. A spot of dried blood divided and multiplied, and the fresh stains scurried around on the sheets like junkyard rats. During these deliriums he mumbled words, but none of his ramblings made any sense to the nurses who were constantly at his side attending him.

For 14 days he teetered near the brink of death. Finally the worst was over, the fever crested, the sickness began to subside, and in its wake only a fragile shell of a young man remained. But as each new day passed, his physical health began to improve. The pounding headache became manageable and the pain in his muscles and joints decreased. His blurred vision cleared. His thinking was not as sluggish as it had been. His appetite improved and he began to add a few pounds to his spindly frame.

Chapter Twelve

Florien Tierney suffered from an irrational fear, believing that when her cancer finally did kill her she would lay dead for days, even weeks, before anyone discovered her remains. She kept asking Red, "Are you getting married?"

"No, I'm not getting married."

"I know you're going to leave me. Stay with me, honey. I'm too sick to find someone else."

"I'm not going anywhere. Don't worry."

Red often reminded herself she was there in Florien's home for one reason and one reason only, to tend her patient's needs. She had been hurt so often in the past by death taking a loved one that Red now tried to shield herself against feeling compassion for this woman who could die at any time.

On days when a friend came to sit with the sick woman, Red was able to escape for a few blessed hours. She almost always rode a cable car to Lacy's Restaurant on Hyde Street. If the weather was warm, she ordered ice cream, and if a cold fog rolled in from off the bay, she sipped coffee and nibbled on fruit pie. Strawberry was her favorite.

Her main recreation was eavesdropping on other people's conversations. One time a pair of married women, seated behind her, discussed the drudgery of their lives and their fear of becoming pregnant with yet another unwanted baby.

"I regret ever getting married," the first woman confided. "My folks pushed me into it. They said any woman over 20 who wasn't married was going to be a sad old maid. I didn't want to end up a sad old maid. I grabbed the first boy who asked me to marry him. Never had an inkling of what I was getting myself into."

"Me, either," the second woman agreed. She lowered her voice. "I never admitted this to anyone—but you're my best friend, the only friend I have in this town—I was pregnant when I married Bill."

"You did *it* before marriage?"

"It's not that I didn't know right from wrong. We were a church-going family and I was well acquainted with the Ten Commandments, forward and backwards. I loosened my morals out of my love for Bill."

"Well, I saved myself. Fred and I went together five years. We never did *it* until after the 'I do's' were said. I made sure of that. But don't get me wrong. He tried. My God, every trick in the book: charming bouquets, love poems, taking me to romantic places. He tried plying me with alcohol, kissing my neck, nibbling my ear, out-and-out begging. I had to be the strong one, the one who kept control.

"For my money, every man is a sex maniac. Swear to God my Fred would be happiest if he kept me barefoot and pregnant. Me, I'd rather see a mad rattlesnake coming through the grass than have that man of mine after me with that lustful look in his eyes."

"Don't I know. Bill never seems to get enough. He treats me like I'm a female dog in heat. I hate that. Just hate it."

As they continued to talk, it seemed to Red that the lives of these two women had been relegated to an endless cycle of washing, baking, canning, gardening, chasing after children and trying to avoid sex with their insatiable husbands. The waitress appeared and asked if Red would like something more. She glanced at the clock on the wall and hurried away, back to the dying woman who had not experienced anything close to sexual fulfillment in umpteen years.

Later, as she recalled the conversation in the restaurant, she was confused as to why the two women loathed the physical act of sex so much, while the ladies she had known at Marge's place seemed to have an unbridled passion for bringing pleasure to a man. True, those ladies were being paid, but she had a suspicion that money was not their only motivating factor. She began to wonder what it would be like if she were to give herself to a man.

⊞⊞⊞⊞⊞⊞

Red was drawn to advertisements for the San Francisco Dating Club. The club was promoted as a place where Christian men and women with high moral values could assemble and get acquainted in a safe and non-threatening environment. Dances were held every Friday, a small admittance fee was charged at the door, and sodas were dispensed at inflated prices. As an inducement the club promised $250 to any couple who met at a dance and subsequently married.

Red joined the club, and after making arrangements for a friend to sit with Florien, she attended a Friday night dance. Here she met a young man, Dave Hastings, who she felt was the most attractive man in attendance. When he asked her to dance, Red had to admit, "I don't know much about dancing, but I'm willing to learn."

"Follow my lead. I'll try not to step on your toes."

As the last dance of the evening ended, Dave gathered Red in his arms and kissed her full on the lips. This caught her completely by surprise. She recoiled, and yet the thrill of the unexpected kiss caused her to tremble.

"May I call you this week?" Dave asked. "We could grab a cup of coffee."

His proposal sounded rather innocent, but she was cautious. "I don't know if I'd feel comfortable giving out the telephone number to someone I just met. But I'll meet you here next Friday night."

⁝⁝⁝⁝⁝⁝⁝

Six days later Florien Tierney lost her ability to see, and by that afternoon she was having trouble breathing. Red sent for the doctor. After his examination, he took her aside and confided, "She doesn't have long."

Red never kept her date with Dave Hastings. Florien died Friday evening and was buried the following Tuesday. After attending the funeral, Red returned to Florien's place, gathered her few belongings and moved into a small apartment. She spent most of her waking hours daydreaming about the thrill of being in Dave's arms, having him waltz her around the dance floor and kissing her tenderly at the end of a long love song.

When the next Friday finally did roll around, Red dressed in a new outfit she bought for the occasion, and rode the cable car to the social club. But when she got there, the door was locked and a *CLOSED* sign was tacked to the wall. Later that week the *Chronicle* newspaper reported that the San Francisco Dating Club had gone into bankruptcy and the officers were under federal indictment for setting up phony marriages and milking the fund dry. After reading the article, Red had a long cry, knowing she would never again see Dave Hastings.

She found employment working as a waitress, and soon became best friends with Tammie Hulse, a fellow waitress and part-time student at San Francisco Business College. The two girls became roommates, living in an affordable room in a woman's dormitory. Tammie slept on the Murphy bed and Red on the couch. Since only students were allowed to live in the dorm, Red enrolled in night school and took a class in shorthand.

A disagreeable housemother strictly enforced the dorm rules. Curfew was 10 o'clock on weeknights and midnight on Friday and Saturday. If a girl was late for curfew, the housemother scolded the offender like a real mother and on Sunday evenings, at mandatory chapter meetings, the good girls added their two cents worth, chiding any offender that loose morals reflected poorly on the entire house.

When girls had free time they gathered and gossiped. They rarely discussed the topic of sex, allowing the subject to be like a low-riding iceberg with only a tiny tip bobbing to the surface every now and then, the great bulk remaining mostly hidden. What they did discuss was romance. The girls coveted romance: flowers, dancing, candlelight, soft kisses and respectful boys. What they indicated they wanted most was to be swept off their feet by a handsome prince, and marriage, children and the security they believed marriage and a family would provide.

Tammie had a steady boyfriend, Billy Wolfe. She had been dating him for almost a year, but he had yet to pop the question. Billy was tall, lanky and self-absorbed. He had been born and raised on the northern California Coast, at Mendocino. His father was a logger, but Billy wanted nothing to do with working in the woods and considered it a disgrace to be the son of a man who felled the mighty redwoods.

Billy was a philosophy major at the University of San Francisco, but his real passion was poetry. He played the part of a poet well and could be amusing or sorrowful, stoic or sentimental. He recited poems with conviction, emotion, and a lyrical cadence that made mere words skip and frolic. To Red, it seemed those words were like beautiful pearls arranged artfully on a string, and she noticed Billy was particularly eloquent when he was drinking. He liked red wine. She had never known a poet. Billy impressed her.

Red and Tammie pooled their tips and bought a hot plate and a small electric oven so they could occasionally cook and entertain in their room. According to dorm rules a boy could be in a girl's room during certain hours, but only if the door remained open. Cooking was strictly forbidden, and yet the housemother overlooked this one transgression, knowing how important it was for a girl to be able to demonstrate her culinary abilities to a prospective mate.

Billy was invited to dinner, but when the roommates counted their money, they could only scrounge together 27 cents between them. Red had been watching apples ripen on a neighbor's tree. She sneaked into their yard and swiped as many as she could carry. That evening they dined on a main course of spaghetti with very little sauce, and had fresh apple cobbler for dessert.

After the meal, Billy continued to sip from a bottle of red wine he had brought with him. He was happy and vocal, reciting some of his more whimsical poetry. Red particularly enjoyed, "*African Jungle, Dawn.*"

> *The lion is king of the jungle*
> *He awakens, stretches pliant muscles*
> *Tawny coat ripples and flows*
> *Sharp claws scratch black earth*
> *He shakes his golden mane*
> *Opens his carnivorous mouth*
> *ROARS!*
> *And all the monkeys in the trees fall dead*

Billy's quirky side was an extraordinary contradiction to the majority of his work. His serious poems he poured out in a passionately sweet, aromatic elixir of syllables and sentences. Red liked to close her eyes when he spoke and envision the cavalcade of images he evoked with words.

At one point during the evening, Tammie excused herself to use the bathroom down the hall. As soon as she was gone, Billy took a gulp of wine and scooted near where Red was sitting cross-legged on the floor. He placed his hands very deliberately on her knees. His eyes sparkled in the candlelight. He leaned so close she could smell the wine on his lips and feel the heat of his breath on her face. He told her, "I want to lay with you on the warm sand on the beach at Mendocino. I want to explore your nakedness. I want to cover and caress your body with my nakedness."

"Is that a poem?"

"No. I'm telling you, I want to lay with *YOU* on the warm sand on the beach at Mendocino. I want to explore *YOUR* nakedness. I want to cover and caress *YOUR* body with *MY* nakedness."

"What about Tammie?"

"I want you. I'm desperate to make love to you. Let me do it to you."

She tried to move away, but Billy made a clumsy grab and caught her by the wrist. She wrenched free, hurriedly got to her feet, took several steps away and glowered at him. "Tammie's my best friend. I wouldn't. I couldn't."

She thought her adamant declaration would dissuade him from pursuing her. It did not. He continued to make her the focal point of his amorous affections until it became such an uncomfortable situation that she began contemplating that her only course of action was to move out.

She went in search of an apartment, but became sidetracked at Belle of the Ball, a fashionable women's apparel shop. Here she found the most wonderful outfit—a lightweight dress with an irregular cut, longer in back and to her knees in front. She tried on the lime-green chiffon, and when matched against the red of her hair, the combination of colors was wonderfully vibrant. Pale yellow heels and pure silk Titian stockings with a dark seam running up the back completed the outfit. She examined herself in front of the full-length mirror and loved the fashionable woman she saw. Before paying for the new outfit, she dabbed on a free sample of lavender perfume, a little behind each ear.

Sauntering down the street she passed store windows that reflected her image and was acutely aware of the men who turned their heads and followed her with their eyes. She felt like a grand lady, despite the fact she was carrying a paper bag stuffed with her old clothes.

She turned the corner onto Beale Street and ran headlong into a policeman coming from the opposite direction. She had been strutting like a stately swan during breeding season, but in the collision she lost her balance and fluttered toward the pavement. The gallant policeman stuck out an arm and snagged her, preventing her fall. It was such a chivalrous move, so casual and easy. All she could do, once she was returned to an upright position, was stand and gaze at her Prince Charming. He was dressed in a blue uniform and was the perfect picture of strength and authority. He was tall, with well-defined features and his hair and mustache were black and as thick as fur. He had penetrating brown eyes that sparkled with what appeared to either be amusement or kindness. He was handsome in the way Gary Cooper or Clark Gable were strikingly handsome.

"Where might you be going in such a hurry?"

The chiffon rippled in a wayward wind and Red busied herself smoothing the dress over her legs. She arched an eyebrow and tried to frame her response to sound offhand and cavalier. "No place in particular. And you, you seemed in a bit of a hurry."

"To the station. To check out. Care to walk along with me?"

She regained her poise. "Not likely." And yet she found this man deliciously appealing and softened her response. "But if you promise to come right back, I suppose I could wait a few minutes for you."

"In a jiffy." He grinned and hurried away.

Over dinner, Red learned his name was Mike McGowan. His bearing, even in civilian clothes, commanded respect. He was 28 years old and had never married, although he admitted he had been close on several occasions. His great-grandfather immigrated to the United States from Ireland during the potato famine of 1846 and came west with the '49ers. He was not one of the lucky few who found his fortune in gold. Instead he became a policeman in San Francisco, as did his son and grandson. Mike was the fourth generation of McGowan men to serve the citizens of San Francisco.

He talked about his work, and family, and made light-hearted jokes. He was friendly, open and genuinely fun to be around. He drank Scotch straight up, so she ordered the same, but after her first sip she requested water to tone it down. They ate, they drank and later they went to see the release of *King Kong*. During the movie he kept refreshing her drink from a hip flask. After the movie ended, she was feeling a little tipsy and more than a trifle sad.

He noticed. "You're crying." He removed a handkerchief from his pocket and dabbed at her moist cheeks.

"That monster, all he wanted was love. And they killed him."

"They sure did. Say, would you care to come to my place and freshen up? It's only 10 minutes from here."

⊡⊡⊡⊡⊡⊡

Mike owned a spacious home on Twin Peaks. Red stood in front of the big bay window and remarked, "The city, the lights, they're so beautiful."

He put a Benny Goodman record on the phonograph, turned the volume low, fixed a pair of drinks and brought one to her. The telephone rang. He answered it. "McGowan's Bar and Grill." He paused a moment. "Sorry, Jake, no cards tonight. Not for me." After another pause he concluded, "Found me a pretty girl and oh, is she sweet. I'm going to spend the next couple of days trying to put a smile on her face."

He winked in her direction and hung up the phone. He came toward her and she purposely turned away from him, pretending to look out the window again, but actually she watched his reflection as he approached and wrapped her in his strong embrace. She gave a rattling purr like a kitten in front of a warm fire and repeated a line she had memorized from a movie. "I didn't come to play. I came to stay."

He laughed. "Let's go to bed."

"I'm not a loose woman." She turned in his arms to face him. "When you promise to marry me, then and only then, will I go to bed with you."

A crazy impulse hit him. He held onto her hands, dropped to one knee, and although he had only known her for only a few fleeting hours, he proposed, "My precious darling, will you marry me?"

"Yes, I will." She giggled and allowed him to sweep her off her feet and carry her into the bedroom where he gently deposited her on the mattress of his four-poster bed. She did not oppose him as he removed the lime-green chiffon dress and

194

skillfully rolled down the silk stockings with the dark seam running up the back.

In the morning, he went out for orange juice and breakfast rolls. She used the phone to call Tammie and tell her the exciting news. She was bursting to tell the whole world. Who else could she call? She thought of Peter and then decided to call Marge Davenport instead.

Marge offered, as a gift to the bride and groom, to foot the bill for the wedding dress as well as a honeymoon wardrobe for the bride. She told Red where to go and gave her the shopkeeper's name.

"Thank you. Thank you. How can I ever repay you?"

"Be happy in life, my sweet dear. Be happy."

┊┊┊┊┊┊┊

Red chose a wedding dress made of ivory georgette and embroidered with silver and crystal beads arranged like the petals of a flower. Her headdress was decorated with beads.

On the day of the wedding, she strolled up the aisle on Peter's arm. Her red hair hung in soft curls against the ivory gown and tiny beads shimmered with each step. She was breathtakingly beautiful and very elegant, aglow with joy and happiness, the epitome of what a bride should look like on her wedding day,

The groom's side of the church was packed with family, friends and fellow officers in dress uniforms. There were only three guests on the bride's side: Tammie, Marge and Helen. It pleased Red to see them there and she never noticed how empty her side of the church appeared.

The ceremony was followed by a three-day honeymoon in Monterey. The couple walked the beach, held hands, kissed in public and made love in private. During those hours of bliss, there was only one chink in the porcelain of their marriage.

That occurred as they were preparing to return home. Red was wearing a chic jersey dress along with strings of flamboyant costume jewelry that accentuated her neck. She splashed on *Shocking* perfume by Italian clothes designer Elsa Schiaparelli, a wedding gift from Helen. When Red had opened the present, she had truly been shocked. The bottle so very much resembled the smooth round curve of a nude female torso, and it had momentarily embarrassed Red.

When Mike saw her, and smelled the perfume, he wrinkled his nose. "You don't have to take a goddamned bath in that stuff. Put a dab here and there, vital spots, let it go at that.

"Another thing, do you have any idea how it looked, you inviting a known madam and one of her hussies to our wedding?"

Red was still reeling from the bite of his initial criticism, and was now caught off guard by the second. He was unmindful and kept talking.

"I'll tell you what. It looked like you were one of them."

"They're my friends. I told you...."

"Yeah, yeah you told me. Okay, for argument's sake, let's just say I believe you. But tell me, what do you imagine everyone was thinking?"

"It's none of their business. I really don't care."

"Well for Christ's sake! Known prostitutes! You should have had the decency to ask my permission."

"Your permission? I didn't know I had to ask your permission whether or not to invite *MY* friends to *MY* wedding."

"Now you know. One last thing, I don't want you wearing gaudy jewelry, backless dresses, short skirts and plunging necklines. I want you to dress like my wife, not some goddamn whore."

Chapter Thirteen

Jack left the hospital in Beaumont, Texas, with a bottle of quinine tablets in hand and instructions to drink plenty of water and take two tablets three times a day. He found the taste of the tablets so godawful bitter that, after taking a handful, he tossed the jar in a drain ditch.

He hitchhiked as far as Dallas, and stood there with his thumb out for five straight hours without catching a ride. Frustrated, and with night coming on fast, he stole a Pontiac sedan from a parking lot and raced to Abilene. He pulled to the curb in front of a movie theater, kept the motor running and the door open, walked the short distance to the ticket booth, and with his hand shoved in his coat pocket, told the girl at the window, "Honey, I've got a gun." He made a jabbing motion with his hand in his pocket. "Give me the money, you don't get hurt." Without hesitation she complied. He pocketed $2.35.

His small-time crime spree, bumping off theater ticket-takers, continued in Albuquerque and again in Phoenix. The two heists netted him seven bucks and change. He sped south and stopped for gas in the tiny town of Hope, Arizona. While paying he noticed a .38 caliber Smith and Wesson revolver hanging from a nail on the wall behind the counter. He nodded toward it and asked the attendant, an old fellow in greasy gray-blue coveralls, "What's the story with the pistol?"

"Collateral. Fellow never came back for it."

"What'll you take?"

"Three bucks."

"Give you two-and-a-half."

"Sold."

Jack bought the pistol even though he had been warned on numerous occasions that a heist man should never carry a weapon because, if you had one, you were liable to use it. If you shot a person while committing a crime and they died, you would likely fry in the electric chair or be hanged with a rope. But he saw the pistol as a convincing tool and swore he'd never buy ammunition for it.

As he crossed into California, his luck began to stretch thin. In the sun-scorched desert town of Blythe,—a town so small it did not have a movie theater—and running low on money for gas and food, he decided on the spur of the moment to knock off the roadhouse on the edge of town. He never bothered to case the joint, merely walked inside with the empty pistol stuffed in his pocket and stepped to the counter.

The bartender was drying his hands on a white bar towel. He looked up, saw Jack and asked, "What's your poison?"

Jack ordered a beer. He picked it up and took a long drink. The bartender wiped at a spot on the polished wood, but it was only something in the grain of the wood and this disturbed him. He frowned because in all his time wiping down the bar he had never seen that particular spot before.

Jack laid money on the bar. The bartender took it and moved away to find out what the newest customer, a bald man who had taken a seat at the bar, wanted to drink. He asked for a beer. As the bartender was pouring it the only woman in the joint came over from where she had been sitting alone in a booth and approached the bald man. It was apparent they knew each other. He smiled and complimented her, saying she was looking fine. She thanked him and performed a pirouette, making it seem like a move she had rehearsed on the dance floor. She was wearing a skirt that hugged her backside and a low-cut red top that made smooth, pretty mounds of her breasts.

He asked if he could buy her a drink. She said she had come over to buy *him* a drink. He said she could catch the next round and asked what she had been doing. She said that her son had moved to Livermore and taken a construction job there, that her house, now that her son was gone, was quiet too much of the time and she was lonely. He put his arm around her waist to console her, and then he swung off the stool and escorted her back to her booth where they sat together.

Jack watched this little drama with indifference. He glanced around the room and saw a handful of customers watching a spirited game of pool. The bartender approached and asked if he wanted another. Jack felt a sudden rush of panic. He knew something was not right, but drew his revolver anyway, eased the barrel over the edge of the counter and pointed it directly at the bartender's belly.

The bartender reacted by throwing his hands in the air and crying out, "Don't shoot! Jesus Christ, don't shoot!"

The woman in the booth saw what was happening and screamed. The bald man jumped to his feet and started to move toward the bar, but Jack barked at him, "Sit down!" He came to an abrupt stop.

"Shut up!" Jack barked at the woman, and she placed her hands over her mouth to stifle her scream. He turned and waved the pistol in the direction of the pool table, ordering the patrons to, "Get your hands where I can see 'em. Everyone, get over against that wall." He spoke to the bald man, "You, too. Move it!" He complied. The woman continued to sit where she was in the booth, both hands clenched firmly over her mouth.

Returning his attention to the bartender, Jack demanded, "Clean out the till. Put it in this." He handed the man a cloth sack with the words "Evansville Flour Company" printed on one side.

A hapless customer chose that moment to stagger through the doorway. He took one halting step and called, "Hey, what the hell's going on here?"

"Don't move! This here's a robbery," Jack shouted. The bartender had shoved a fistful of bills into the flour sack. Jack grabbed the sack and moved away, walking backward, waving the gun, barking at the patrons who stood between him and the door, "Get out of my way." Then he was outside, starting the stolen Pontiac and speeding away.

A few miles down the road he turned on the radio hoping to take his mind off the robbery. But the only station he found on the dial spit static in the background as a preacher delivered a fire and brimstone message that had a cadence and tempo so distinctive and precise it could have been played at a dance. Jack tried finding something else, failed and snapped the dial off. When he returned his attention to the road, flashing lights were coming toward him and he was afraid, but his fears proved unfounded as an ambulance shot past, its red light throbbing like a severed artery.

Roaring through Ripley and Palo Verde, Jack reached a fork in the road and made the quick decision to turn west toward Brawley. He figured the cops would never look in Brawley, not with the Mexican border so close. Upon reaching town he relaxed. He enjoyed a sit-down dinner of liver and onions at a small diner, and then went to the movie theater where he watched a double feature: Edward G. Robinson in *Little Caesar* and James Cagney in *Public Enemy*. Both were gangster films glorifying the life of crime, but in the last reel of *Public Enemy* federal agents swoop in and gun down a swaggering James Cagney in a hail of machine gun bullets.

As he left the show house, Jack was thinking maybe he should ditch the Pontiac. Then again he reasoned he would drive it into the mountains, to the diggings where he planned to mine gold. If he needed it gone, he could always shove it over a cliff. When he reached the Pontiac, he opened the door and slipped behind the wheel. As he went to turn the key his attention was diverted to a man approaching from his left. Instinct made him to turn to his right. Another man was approaching from that direction. When he looked over the hood two men had stepped in front of the Pontiac and they were leveling Tommy guns at the windshield. Jack, very deliberately, lifted his hands and raised them. The man on the driver's side yanked opened the door. One hand held a revolver and the other a leather case that he flipped open to reveal a nickel-plated badge.

"You're under arrest for armed robbery."

Jack was taken to jail. While awaiting trial he suffered a relapse of malaria and was hospitalized for several weeks. At his trial he pled not guilty, but it was an open-and-shut case when the roadhouse bartender and four customers, including the bald man and the woman he was with, positively identified Jack as the robber. The jury deliberated only a few minutes before bringing back a guilty verdict. The judge was all too quick to impose the maximum allowable sentence, 12 years plus one day at Folsom Prison. With good behavior, Jack might be released in 10.

Folsom had an ugly reputation. The convicts referred to it as Bloody Folsom, because if a con got sideways with a guard—the cons called them *screws*—the con was liable to vanish into an unmarked grave. If anyone did inquire, the matter was taken care of with a little paperwork and the death recorded as *Died of Natural Causes*.

When there was trouble, the *screws*—many were only a thin cut above the criminals they were paid to guard—were trained to shoot first and sort out the bodies when they were on the ground. Every year or two the cons mounted an uprising and killed a few screws, making sure they died slowly. In the end the riots were crushed and the cons were forced to pay a heavy price for their insurrection.

Captain Ryan was the guard who processed Jack. He was a tall thin man with eyes the color of emeralds and his profile was reminiscent of President Abraham Lincoln on the head of a penny. He was an exception to a lot of the other screws because he had the capacity to feel compassion.

Captain Ryan ordered Jack to strip down and when he saw the prosthesis his eyes widened. He said, "Take it off. Give it to me."

Captain Ryan held the artificial leg at eye level, peered at it, tapped it here and there with his knuckles, and when satisfied there were no hidden compartments, he handed it back, explaining, "We've got to make sure no contraband gets smuggled inside."

Jack's clothes and valuables were placed in a bag. The bag was sealed. He was issued prison blues, and after he was dressed, Captain Ryan walked him into the general population wing. Men whistled and jeered. Walking along the second tier, shadowy faces became visible between bars with eyes as menacing as dark caves. There were no colors, only strange levels of darkness—black, gray and indistinct, formless shadows.

With a jangle of keys, Captain Ryan opened the barred door to the cell. Jack stepped inside. The door slammed shut with a resolute solidness that caused a shudder to race along his spine. Again the keys jangled. Then the captain walked away. For a moment Jack stood listening to the retreating footfalls, then sat on the edge of the bunk. His elbows went on his knees and his head dropped into his hands. Around him the insolent noises of confined men began to buzz, a low drone like flies drawn to spoiled meat.

He was aware of his shallow, ragged breathing and could smell the staleness of the air. The cold reality of his predicament hit him hard—Folsom Prison, this cell, was to be his home for the next decade or so—and when it was over he would have nothing to show except years of his life pissed away.

Tugging at the back of his mind was an image of Kelsey standing over his hospital bed, telling him everything was going to be fine. But everything was not going to be fine. Kelsey had traded away his rambling ways and in return he now probably had a steady job, a pretty wife, a house with a little lawn he mowed every Saturday morning and kids to play ball with and take fishing. Kelsey had it all. Jack had this barred cubicle and a locked door. Ten goddamn years.

His chest ached. His heart beat hard and fast. Jack told himself to calm down. He tried to remember times in his life when he had been happy. Was there ever a time he had been happy? He didn't know. A memory came to mind. Nebraska; it was a bluebird day with a solitary white cloud, a small puffy thing, hanging up there and everywhere sandhill cranes dancing, stirring the air with their wings, giving that tremulous and intoxicating mating call, filling every corner of the world to overflowing with noise and vibrations.

There was another moment of pleasure. He was very young, standing at the window and watching his mother pick a bouquet from the flower garden. She held in her hands a rainbow of colors. She must have felt his gaze because she turned, saw him at the window and her face became a radiant smile. And in that moment, he knew his mother loved him.

"Knock off the fuckin' blubbering. Act like a man," barked the con in the adjoining cell.

The following day Jack was assigned to work in the pit, given an eight-pound maul and directed to make little rocks out of big rocks. He impressed the screws with his hard work and determination to match the efforts of the able-bodied men on either side of him.

One evening, as Captain Ryan was making his rounds, he paused in front of Jack's cell. Jack was sitting on his bunk reading a book.

"Hear you're pulling your weight in the pit."

"I try."

"What you reading?"

"*Cow Country.*"

"I've always admired Will James. He knows what it's like to be a cowboy. He lived the life."

"He's a darn good artist, too."

"Jack, I've been keeping an eye on you. What impresses me most, besides your work ethic, is that you've never asked for preferential treatment on account of your leg. I've never heard you complain, not even once. I think that kind of attitude should be rewarded. If you want to start taking classes toward earning your high school diploma, and maybe get some college credit too, I'll arrange for an educational transfer. You'd be assigned to me, attend classes and be responsible for cleaning the walkway in Cell Block One. What do you think? Interested?"

"Sure. Yeah. I'll do it."

Jack was assigned to duty in Cell Block One, the wing housing the most violent offenders. Twice a day he swept the walkway and mopped it every other day. When not sweeping or mopping, he spent his time studying in what was known as the *topping room*, the slang term for the room where the death penalty was carried out. He and the other students sat at a long table, in the shadow of the gallows, working to complete correspondence courses offered through the University of California. He studied math, biology, world history and creative writing.

He had little contact with the inmates of Cell Block One. For the most part the men were sullen and uncommunicative. When their appeals ran out, they were destined to serve life sentences or face the death penalty. One day as Jack was sweeping, Elvin Dickson, the most feared man in Bloody Folsom, called to him.

Jack took a single hesitant step toward the black man's cell, and stopped. He figured Elvin wanted him to deliver a message to another prisoner. He sometimes did that as a favor to inmates.

"Heard you're doin' book learnin'."

"Correspondence courses. I'm working at it."

"I wanna be able to read them law books and find out if my lawyers are playin' straight. Suppose you could learn me to read?"

Jack began teaching Elvin and before a month had transpired, he had 14 students from Cell Block One in his class. The students learned about Jack's history as a boxer and encouraged him to become involved in the Folsom Boxing Club. The club had been sanctioned by the administration with the hope such a program would be a good physical release for the prisoners, a way for them to work out their anger and aggression short of rioting.

Jack started working out in the prison gym. At first he was content to train on the heavy bag and the speed bag, but he began to wonder how he'd stack up against some of the other boxers. One of his students chided, "Come on, *Teach*. Let's see what you got. Strap on the gloves with me."

Jack accepted the challenge, crawled in the ring and sparred a couple rounds. In the process he rediscovered the fun of pitting himself against another man. He also recognized and appreciated the coordination it took to throw a good combination, the evasiveness involved in slipping a punch, the intricacy of a good fake, and the courage it took to take a punch and deliver a better one. He loved it all, and before the sparring session was over, men were gathered around the ropes chanting, "Teach! Teach! Teach! Teach!"

Max Baer had once called Jack, pound-for-pound, the best fighter on the planet. The men of Cell Block One dubbed him as *pound-for-pound, the toughest man in the joint*. Few men in Folsom were in the lightweight class, and when Jack continued his training he usually had to step up to the welterweight, and sometimes even the middleweight division to get a good workout.

A new program was instituted to bring fighters from the outside to fight inside the walls at Folsom. Jack signed up and was scheduled to fight Iron Man Johnson, a fighter with 11 professional fights under his belt, 10 wins by way of knockout. Johnson's manager was planning to use the cons as cheap and expendable sparring partners.

On the night of the big fight, Elvin was Jack's corner man. He warned, "Work the body. Go inside, get tight, stay tight, take away his power. Don't never step back."

Johnson was tall and lanky, a true middleweight, with well-defined muscles and a jaw like a granite boulder. Jack fought the first round as instructed, and for most of the second he followed suit. But then, to set up a hook, he took a half step back and gave a little bob of his head. Johnson was well schooled and did not fall for the fake. He brought a left hand straight up the open alleyway and caught Jack flush on his right temple. His good leg turned to rubber. He went down and he could not rise before the count reached 10.

That night, as Jack relived the fight or what he could remember of it, the thing that bothered him most was not that he lost, but that he never saw that straight left coming. He knew he could kid himself, say he was rusty from his years out of the ring, or blame it on his bad leg, or the fact he was fighting out of his weight class, or even that Iron Man Johnson was a better fighter. But he never saw the punch coming!

Jack had known fighters who hung on past their prime and took a beating because they failed to see the punches and therefore could not mount a defense. He knew his boxing skills had eroded, recognized and accepted that fact. Thinking he wanted to stay active in the sport, he asked Captain Ryan if he could become a trainer.

Ryan stroked the point of his thin chin. "I think you'd be short-changing yourself. Looking over the work you've accomplished in your correspondence courses, I can see you have a gift. It's impressive, truly impressive. You're a voracious reader, and it's my belief you're a natural born writer."

"Don't you think I'd be a good trainer?"

"You say you want to stay in the fight game? Fine. Every week guys from the outside come here to fight. What do we know about them? For instance, did you know Iron Man Johnson is currently the 27th ranked middleweight in the world? And how about the other guys who come in here to fight? What makes them tick? Why are they willing to visit Folsom Prison and stand toe-to-toe with the meanest men alive? Aren't you curious? Don't you want to know? You should be interviewing fighters and writing stories for the newspaper. Have you ever read the prison rag?"

Jack shook his head. "I've seen it, just never thought about...never figured I'd be good enough for something like that. Never crossed my mind."

"Oh, you're good enough. Start by interviewing fighters and writing about the fight game, branch out and see where it takes you. Hell, you might find you're a newspaper man at heart and end up with a legitimate career once you get out of here."

"Guess it's something I ought to consider anyway."

"You need to do more than that. You need to act on it."

"You really think I can?"

"Absolutely. As of tomorrow you are assigned as a stringer for the *Folsom Gazette*."

Chapter Fourteen

Jack wrote several stories and tossed each in the garbage can, but when he finished a story on the tragic life of Sweet Candy Anderson—what he remembered from his days as his sparring partner, as well as information he gleaned from cons who had known Anderson in later years—Jack asked Captain Ryan if he would read his story.

His story, *Desperation*, told of the fighter's rise to become one of the top ten middleweights in the world. The big fight, the big break, never came for Sweet Candy. He hung on too long and turned to alcohol to mollify his pain and disappointments.

"One hell of a story! You captured the glory and the fame, as well as the downside of the game. You got me there at the end."

††††††††

The *Folsom Gazette* published the story and five weeks later the warden was notified that Jack Small's story had received top honors for a biographical feature at the Northern California Newspaper Association's annual awards banquet. Jack was sent a commemorative plaque, but it was against the rules for a convict to have anything metal that might be fashioned into a shiv or some other dangerous weapon. Captain Ryan said he would keep the award in his office.

He sent for Jack and nodded toward the plaque hanging on the wall. He said, "From now on, one of your duties will be to sweep my office. That way you can see your commendation whenever you want, and know the top people in the newspaper industry found value in your writing."

⣏⣛⣛⣛⣛⣛⣹

Late on the morning of December 7, 1941, Jack was busy sweeping Captain Ryan's office. A guard rushed in wanting to know where the captain was. Jack knew something was drastically wrong and feared a breakout, or that a riot was erupting.

"What's the matter?"

"Goddamn dirty Japs attacked Pearl Harbor, trapped our Pacific fleet at anchor and killed the hell out of our men. We're smack dab in the middle of another World War."

It took time, but eventually the effects of the United States entering World War II reached inside the walls of Folsom Prison. With all able-bodied civilian men in uniform and sent overseas to fight the enemy, domestic farm laborers were in short supply. Food was essential to the war effort and trusted inmates were drafted to help with the harvests.

Jack was among the first to be sent out from Folsom on work detail. The men were taken to a nearby apple orchard and loaded onto a wagon pulled by a tractor. At the end of each row of trees were ladders, picking bags and stacks of bushel baskets. Prisoners were dropped off, one to a row, and instructed to pick each tree clean before moving on.

After working all day, the men were returned to the prison. Later, when they were sent to Murdock's farm near Marysville, the distance was too great to return to the prison and the men were housed in a bunkhouse. A lucky few had beds, but most of the 50 men were given blankets and slept on the floor. Other accommodations also left a lot to be desired: a single two-holer served as a latrine, a cattle trough was converted to a wash basin and the men sat at long tables to eat. The kitchen was a portable unit sent from the prison and staffed by convicts.

Jim Murdock, the owner of the farm, had lost a leg in a farm accident. He recognized Jack's stiff-ankle gait, the way he swung his left leg, and guessed he also wore an artificial limb. On the third day of harvest, after the evening meal had been served, Jack was sitting by himself under a tree reading a book. Jim walked over and sat nearby on the grass.

"Howdy. How ya doin'?"

"Fine. How 'bout you?"

"Better since you boys arrived to help. Don't know what I'd have done." Jim shrugged. "Lose the crop, I suppose."

"We appreciate getting out, being able to put in a hard day's work. I forgot how good it feels to accomplish something." Jack set the book aside.

"I don't mean to be out of line, but I thought I'd just tell you, I admire the way you get up and down the picking ladders. I've got one of my own." Jim rapped his knuckles against his wooden leg.

"It doesn't slow me down much."

"I can see it doesn't. So, where you from?"

"Nebraska."

"I'll be darned. Me too. Where?"

"Albion. That's where I was born. Raised some in Denver, but consider Hastings home."

"You know where Columbus is?"

"Of course."

"I was born and raised in a little burg between Columbus and Norfolk, place called Creston. Ever hear of it?"

"Can't say as I have."

"We left out of there just before the Depression. Lucky we did. So, what's your story?"

Jack mulled over what he should tell and settled for, "My folks divorced when I was young. Mother moved us to Denver. She remarried. We moved back to Nebraska."

The men continued to talk even after the sky turned gold with streaks of orange and red. Not until it was nearly dark did Jack shuffle off to the bunkhouse and Jim return to his house and family.

The following day, Jim once again came around after dinner, bringing his 3-year-old son Skippy with him. While the men talked, Skippy dug in the ground, moving dirt around with a stick.

Jack mentioned how difficult it was to sleep in the bunkhouse with 50 snoring men and someone continually getting up, stepping over those on the floor to use the chamber pots kept at one end of the long room. He admitted he was having difficulty getting a good night's rest.

Jim spoke to the supervisor of the prison crew, said he could use a hand with chores and asked specifically for Jack. When his request was granted, he added, "Rather than rousting him early and inconvenience everyone in the bunkhouse, how about if he sleeps in the barn?"

That evening Jack lay in a comfortable depression in a small mountain of hay. He breathed in the sweet aroma of summer, listened to cows munch hay and horses grind rolled oats between their strong teeth. As he slept, a fast-moving cloud dumped rain that gleefully drummed the tin roof. At the first signs of dawn, the pigeons stirred among the rafters and mourning doves began to coo.

Jack helped with chores and told his new friend, "Last night was the first good sleep I've had in years. I'd take a hay loft over the finest bed in any luxury hotel in the world."

When the last apple had been picked, Jim shook Jack's hand.

"One of these days they'll turn you loose. I want you to remember this: when the chess game is decided, the king and the pawn go back in the same box. Don't ever put yourself down because you made mistakes. You've paid for your mistakes many times over."

Jack returned to Folsom and the dull routine of structured life on the inside. Several uneventful months passed and then he was called into Captain Ryan's office. The captain told him, "Have a seat. Well, apparently you made a favorable impression on Jim Murdock. He wrote the members of the parole board recommending your sentence be reduced to time served. You probably don't know this, but the Murdock family has contributed liberally to the campaigns of several state politicians. The name carries considerable weight, if you get my drift.

"The parole board is meeting today at 3 o'clock. They're going to review your case and requested you be there."

Jack walked into the room where the parole board met. Two members were seated behind a long conference table. Jack stood nervously before them. Several minutes passed and then one of the men finally looked up.

"We have received letters asking us to review your file." He pawed through numerous papers. "You have served a majority of your sentence. Am I correct?"

"Yes, sir."

"You have many flattering reports," the second board member said. "You've earned nearly enough college credits for a journalism degree, have taught other inmates, worked on the harvest crew and been a model prisoner." He picked up a letter. "Captain Ryan believes you have been rehabilitated. Mr. Small, do you honestly believe you have been rehabilitated?"

"Yes, sir, I do."

The first man said, "If your sentence was reduced, could you assure this board you would make the most of your future?"

"Yes, sir."

"And what would you do?"

"Sir, I'd like to get into the newspaper business."

"I see you received a writing award from the Northern California Newspaper Association. That is a pretty prestigious award, isn't it, Mr. Small?"

"Yes, sir, it certainly is."

"You're dismissed."

The second man added, "Once the paperwork is completed, you will be a free man. Don't blow this opportunity Mr. Small, because there is no such thing as a second chance."

"Thank you. I promise you, I'll make the most of it."

When he departed Folsom Prison, Jack was wearing new underwear, a white shirt, tie-up shoes and a brown suit. He took the bus to Sacramento and bought a train ticket to Grand Island, Nebraska. He was going home.

Chapter Fifteen

It was an envelope that Grace received while they were living in Denver that eventually led the family to pull up stakes and move to Hastings, Nebraska. Inside the envelope was a formal notice from an attorney that Grace's Aunt Melva, had passed away. Grace had been designated as the sole beneficiary of her estate; an estate that included a house and two acres of scrub pasture on the outskirts of Hastings, Nebraska. Melva was Grace's father's sister. She never married and lived in Hastings with a woman companion. Only one time had they ever come to Chicago to visit.

After receiving the letter and reading it, Grace went to her bedroom and tucked it in her dresser, secreting it beneath her stockings. As she slid the drawer shut she glanced in the oval mirror and absently smoothed a few loose hairs in place. She thought maybe she would pretty herself up.

That evening she fixed Chet meatloaf with potatoes and gravy. She baked him a chocolate cake. The children were put to bed early and then, over coffee and cake, she brought out the letter. After he had read the letter, she championed that this was an opportunity for them to start a new life.

"It's for the best. I know you can find work in Hastings. And I can do something to help out. At least we'll have a place of our own where we can live and no rent hanging over our heads. It will be wonderful for the children. Please."

"I don't think so. I was born here, raised here. I'm a Denver guy. What would I do in some burg in Nebraska? Not enough excitement for me. If I were to move anywhere it'd be California. I've got the talent to jump into the movie business."

"I know you do. This would be a temporary thing. We get our feet on the ground and then we can talk about California."

Chet wrestled with the decision and eventually came to the conclusion his primary responsibility, as a husband and father, was to provide for his family. Free rent was a step in the right direction. He rubbed the stubble on his chin, resigned himself to the inevitable.

"Okay, we'll give it a try. But if it doesn't work out, we sell the place and move on."

┣┿┿┿┿┿┥

When they did move to Hastings, Chet walked around town and concluded it was little more than an irrelevant speck of dust on the vast sweep of the Great Plains. The business district was a collection of brick buildings plunked down thoughtlessly between the Platte and the Little Blue Rivers. He squandered time observing a few adventuresome squirrels that had given up hibernation to skim over piles of filthy snow, patches of brown grasses and race through the sprawling skeletons of elm and cottonwood trees. The branches threw thin veined shadows on the ground, lonely blue shadows that served to amplify his personal misery and feelings of separation from the good life he had enjoyed in Denver.

Chet found work as a clerk at Callahan's Hardware Store, an establishment stocked with everything a rural customer could possibly need: a National washboard, corsets, shoelaces, nuts, bolts, screws and dill pickles in a stone crock. Still, he was not happy. One evening he complained to Grace, "It seems like all I do is sell shovels to farmers, mouse traps to farmers' wives and dispense two-for-a-penny candy to their obnoxious kids. Everyone who steps through the door has manure on their boots and hayseeds in their hair. That's all this is...a damn hayseed town."

"You're exaggerating."

"The hell I am!" He moved in the direction of the door. A moment later he was swallowed by night, a place where noisy crickets beat their wings together, an alley cat screeched defiantly from the top of a board fence, and a bat swooped low to swallow a bug. Heading uptown, he walked to the back door of Owen's Barbershop, where some of the locals gathered to smoke, chew, spit, drink moonshine and play two-bit poker. He sat in on the card game and drank to be sociable. The alcohol seemed to coat the nerve endings of his soul. It was a painkiller that mollified him for the time being, but he did not know how much longer he could exist in Hastings, Nebraska.

⋮⋮⋮⋮⋮⋮⋮

A farmer gave Jack a lift from the Grand Island depot to the crossroad near the small town of Hastings. The farmer drove away, but Jack remained rooted to the shoulder of the road, staring at the town in the distance. Dawn was breaking.

Jack walked a ways, until he saw the open field where the town of Hastings once held a Chautauqua assembly, a celebration that took place in the waning days of a hot August and was housed in a revival tent rented from a preacher in Topeka. The Chautauqua was the Hastings social event of that year, and any local person with even an ounce of talent, and enough guts to climb on stage, was expected to entertain the crowd.

Among notable performances were 84-year-old Hap Zigfeld playing his fiddle, the tap-dancing of 8-year-old fireball Tillie Moore, an emotional plea by a local druggist to enlist the public's support for developing a national highway system, a religious housewife who gave an impassioned dissertation warning of the evils of smoking cigarettes, and a respected banker cautioning investors that the big bull market was subject to fail under the weight of margins, margins being the popular method of purchasing stocks with a down payment of only ten cents on the dollar.

Jack had ridden his bicycle to the Chautauqua. For a while he watched grasshoppers spring off the hardpan to rattle and snap. Only occasionally did he bother to poke his head inside the tent to catch bits and pieces of the festivities. Nellie and several of her friends sat on chairs and played dolls. Donny stayed close to his mother. It seemed that Grace, more than any other member of the family, enjoyed herself. One of her favorite skits featured a number of locally prominent businessmen—storekeepers, bankers and teachers—who coated their faces, arms and hands with lamp black and performed in padded bras and short skirts as the *Ebony Steppers*, a line of Negro chorus girls who were, at that time, starring on Broadway in New York City.

Chet periodically stepped outside the tent to stand in the shadows and take short pulls from his hip flask. He favored the comedy acts, and if they were a bit racy, he liked it all the more. A skit was performed by a boy and a girl, who came on stage dressed in raccoon skin coats commonly worn by the college crowd. In a sweet but naughty tone the girl sang, "She doesn't drink. She doesn't pet. She hasn't been to college yet."

The boy and girl took turns acting the part of the straight man.

Girl: "Do you think your son will soon forget all he learne⟨ at college?"

Boy: "I sure hope so. He can't make a living necking and drinking."

Girl: "Marriage is an institution."

Boy "Marriage is love. Love is blind."

Girl: "Therefore, marriage is an institution for the blind."

The girl hiked up the hem of her coat and skirt to show off a shapely calf. She spoke in an amorous way to the young man, "Do you consider my legs long?"

Boy: "Yes, whenever I can and for as long as possible."

After the final mid-day performance, the crowd made its way to the potluck dinner laid out on borrowed tables. Grace looked around for Chet, wanting to have dinner with him, but he was nowhere to be seen. She had thought the Chautauqua would have been the perfect event for him, a place for him to showcase his many and varied talents. She had encouraged him to participate, but he let her know in no uncertain terms that he was above contributing to the entertainment of the citizens of Hastings.

Apparently he changed his mind—the alcohol he consumed that day might have had something to do with his decision to perform—because, after dessert had been served, he stepped to the podium. He was dressed in his dark blue suit and a wide red-and-white striped tie. His shoes were freshly shined and his hair was slicked back.

"Ladies and gentlemen, the first poem I wish to recite for you is, *O, My Luve's Like A Red, Red Rose* by Robert Burns.

> *O, my Luve's like a red, red rose,*
> *That's newly sprung in June:*
> *O, my Luve's like the melodie*
> *That's sweetly play'd in tune...."*

His delivery came across with all the youthful spirit of a lad in love and the crowd returned to their seats in the big tent to enjoy Chet's splendid delivery and the forceful way in which he articulated the written words of the masters. At the end they responded with a thunderous standing ovation. Well-wishers rushed forward.

"God has blessed you with a truly wonderful gift. Thank you for sharing it with us," an elderly woman said.

"A command performance," a gentleman said. "I have never been so moved in my entire life. Thank you."

"You were absolutely fantastic," an attractive woman in a bright green dress gushed. She gave him a hasty peck on his cheek.

While Chet relished in that praise, his family stood off to one side, out of the limelight. Grace hoped that, with this outpouring of admiration and appreciation, her husband would now feel as though he was a solid part of the community.

░░░░░░

The children were tucked in their beds and their prayers had been said. Chet sipped a highball and told Grace, "I'm quitting the hardware store. I'm going into business for myself."

She was immediately apprehensive about this turn of events, but she also was well aware that after his performance at the Chautauqua, the bright shimmer of Chet's star was on the rise. It was in her best interest to be meek, submissive and supportive. "Whatever you want, honey."

Chet's entire life had revolved around selling and performing. He worked to make selling the greatest of all art forms. It was Sinclair Lewis who stated: "The cosmic purpose of selling is not the act of selling anything in particular for or to anybody in particular, but simply the act of selling." He must

have formed this hypothesis after having met Chet Harmon, or someone very much like him.

Before a week had passed, Chet talked his way into buying, on time and with no money down, a flatbed Ford, three-quarter ton truck. Each morning he rose before dawn, drove through the countryside purchasing produce from farmers and returning to Hastings to sell that produce. He soon developed a regular route, with many housewives only too eager to purchase carrots, peas, lettuce, onions, beans, and corn from such a celebrated and charismatic man as Chet Harmon. Even if they had gardens in their own backyards, they still bought a little of this and a little of that.

During potato harvest or when the apples were ripe, Chet brought Jack along to help with the lifting and toting. It was on one of those days that Chet, after instructing Jack to "Stay put in the rig, I'll be back sooner or later," disappeared for well over an hour. Jack became curious and went searching. He spotted his stepfather coming out the back door of a house, tucking his shirt in his trousers as he skipped down the steps. A woman appeared from behind a screen door and called his name. He went back and kissed her. Jack watched all this from over the top of a back alley fence. Then he ran to the Ford so Chet would never suspect he had been caught red-handed.

⊞⊞⊞⊞⊞⊞

Now as Jack walked toward Hastings, a dog barked and an airplane took off, circled overhead and flew south. A kid on a bicycle pedaled up the street, flinging folded newspapers onto porches with a well-practiced aim. Women in bathrobes pushed open doors, stepped outside to retrieve newspapers and bring in jugs of fresh milk for breakfast.

The residential section of Hastings was nearly the same as Jack remembered, except newer-modeled cars were parked along the tree-lined streets. The business district had changed considerably, with signs advertising new businesses and there were buildings in places where he remembered empty lots. McMurray's Hardware was now a fancy new showroom and an overhead sign advertised "Conger Olds and Pontiac Dealership."

Jack stepped to the glass, put his hands around his face to cut the glare and peered inside. He saw a lamp illuminating one of the offices and someone sitting there. He moved until he could make out his friend, Kelsey Conger, who only vaguely resembled the boyhood friend from Jack's memory. Kelsey was in the process of losing most of his hair. He had put on considerable weight and his face looked soft and pudgy. When he happened to glance up and saw Jack, he broke into a broad grin.

The two friends embraced. Kelsey stepped back. "Well look at you." His eyes moved over Jack's loose fitting clothes. It was easy to tell the body underneath was slender and the suit, although wrinkled and with a lived-in look to it, gave Jack the false neatness of a mechanic who had recently washed with Lava soap.

"Let's go down to the bakery," Kelsey suggested.

While they sipped coffee and nibbled fresh pastries, Jack asked a string of questions. Kelsey answered, and it was revealed that Kelsey was married to Robin, a redhead from Council Bluff. They had three children and a new house with a big mortgage. Apparently Kelsey could afford a high lifestyle. The war had sent wheat prices skyrocketing and farmers were beating a path to the dealership door to buy any car they could get their hands on. On top of that, the government was working three shifts making bombs at the naval ammunition depot a few miles from town. Workers were paid well and spent money freely. Business had never been better.

"I'm investing in land. God only made so much of it. All it can do is go up in price. Right now I'm concentrating on farm ground, but I realize when the war is over, grain will take a nosedive. I buy land when it's affordable.

"Here's another thing, I don't limit myself to farm ground. I pick up residential property when I can. Hey, people have to have a place to live. The way I got it figured, when the war ends, all those soldiers are coming home. I'll sell them a new car. Then they'll find girlfriends, get married and start families. And I'll be right there to sell them a house.

"Did I tell you, I almost got drafted, but Dad stepped in and said he needed me to run the store? Then he got sick and I had the whole kit-and-caboodle. Robin and I had Abigail, along came Dennis and finally little Sammy. You better believe there've been plenty of times I've been tempted to run off and enlist."

Kelsey was grinning. He inquired, "So what's up with you?"

"That'd take a while."

Kelsey lowered his voice and leaned forward. "Heard through the grapevine you ran afoul of the law."

"Tell you all about that sometime. What I'd like to find out is what happened to my family. Been a lot of grain down the chute; guess I kinda lost track."

Kelsey became solemn. "You had Chet pegged all along. He got mixed up with some hot-blooded Cajun woman—husband caught them in the act—and before the dust settled they were long gone. Chet and the gal end up in Alabama, Georgia, someplace down south. That's all I know."

"And Momma?"

"You know, I don't think she ever got over losing that no good son of a bitch. Far as I know, she never had the company of another man after Chet pulled out. Guess she always held out hope he'd come home."

Jack didn't want to ask but he did. "Where is she?"

"Consumption took her two, no, three years ago."

For a long moment Jack studied a woman bouncing a baby on her knee in a nearby booth. He drew a stinging breath and let it out slowly. "Where's she buried?"

"Here. You remember where it is?"

Jack nodded. "And Nellie and Donny?"

"Donny's playing ball over in Topeka for a semi-pro team. Doing real good from what I hear. Heck of a ball player, catcher. Hits the ball a country mile, I kid you not.

"Nellie, she got herself married. Husband works for a fertilizer dealer in Roseland. They've got one kid and she's expecting another any day now. She'll be tickled pink to see you. She always idolized the hell out of you.

"When I came home, after your accident, your mom hounded me, but you told me not to say anything. I never did. Guess you finally wrote a letter, so I went ahead and filled in the details. Didn't figure it made any difference at that point.

"Unless a person knew you had lost...you don't limp, not hardly any at all. Damn, you're looking healthy, Jack. Wish I was in the shape you're in, but sitting behind the desk like I do.... So tell me, Jack, how come you came home?"

"See the place. See the family. See you...."

"Gonna stick around?"

"Don't know."

"Hey, buddy, I could use another salesman. I was just telling Robin last night...."

Jack stopped him. "I want to try the newspaper business. I've had some experience."

"Where at?"

"West Coast."

"Fred Soodel is the editor of the *News Tribune*. He's a personal friend of mine. I'll put in a good word for you."

"Thanks. I'll probably need all the help I can get."

The two friends lingered a while longer, and it was a little like old times when they used to sit in the open doorway of a boxcar and watch the countryside roll past. There was a comfortable feeling between them, and yet they both recognized a mild undercurrent of tension. Kelsey regretted abandoning Jack after the accident and coming home. He also felt a twinge of guilt about his personal success. On the other hand, Jack felt he had squandered his life and questioned whether he could ever measure up to Kelsey.

Jack dug four-bits from his pocket and laid it on the table. Kelsey told him, "Put it away." He called to the waitress. "Rachel, put it on my tab will you?"

Chapter Sixteen

Red was convinced Mike wanted a child. She tried to get pregnant, but it never happened. Out of sheer frustration, she finally made a doctor's appointment. That evening she turned toward her husband and asked him a question. She did not really expect an answer.

"Do you know what a cervix is?"

His eyes took on a faraway look, as if he was sighting down a pool cue to make sure it was straight.

"Some female part."

"Silly word isn't it? Cervix. Sounds like a foreign language. Greek maybe. I went to the doctor today. He said my cervix is misshapen. He said I'll never be able to have children."

She was standing at the sink, busily twisting a dishtowel in her hands. It was as if the towel was somehow the culprit, the cause of her infertility. "I was thinking we could adopt a baby, maybe an orphan that nobody wants."

Mike slammed his open palm on the table with such force his glass jumped and Scotch sloshed over the rim. "I don't give a good goddamn what you think. I'm not about to take in someone else's problem. Hell, I've got enough of my own."

A few months later, Red smelled perfume on one of his shirts, and there were other times she noticed lipstick smudges. Still she could not bring herself to confront him, believing, if push came to shove, he might very well choose his girlfriends over his barren wife. She became more and more withdrawn.

One day, feeling unhappy and depressed, Red telephoned her friend Helen, and unloaded her troubles, confessing her inability to conceive and her suspicions Mike was having a string of wild affairs. When she finally got around to asking for advice, she fully expected her friend to say, "Kick the bum out. File for divorce." But Helen shocked her.

"Take him to bed."

"What?

"Take him to bed."

"But I'm so angry."

"Forget. Forgive. Make him happy. Tell him he's the greatest lover in the world. Scream like a wildcat and pant like a dog. Make him think you can't get enough."

"Really?"

"Yes. We're talking about saving your marriage."

"I don't believe I'm that good of an actress."

"Yes, you are; just play to his ego."

Red took the advice to heart, but discovered, in the bedroom, what her husband needed from a wife was far different than what he needed from a girlfriend. A wife was to be his home port and the girlfriends were snug little harbors where he could duck into anytime a storm threatened.

The Catholic religion did not allow for divorce, and Mike rationalized his unfaithfulness with a conviction that every man has the right to step outside the boundaries of a marriage that is not working. He told himself, if Red had been capable of having a son to carry on the family name and continue the tradition of a McGowan as a San Francisco police officer, that might have been enough to keep him home.

Red, as she had done before, sought escape through movies, slipping into the black void of theatres and watching make-believe worlds whirl to life on the silver screen. Here each story had a beginning, a conflict in the middle and a satisfying resolution. For a few brief hours, she could become Marlene Dietrich as Lola, the nightclub performer in *The Blue Angel* who led astray a saintly professor. She could be Mae West in *My Little Chickadee*, coyly fending off the lecherous W. C. Fields. She could be Vivien Leigh as Scarlett O'Hara in *Gone With the Wind*, running across the plantation lawn after learning the man she loved was marrying another. But when the movie ended and the credits rolled, she was always forced to return to the sad certainty of her loveless marriage and the empty house on Twin Peaks.

She was watching a movie the day Mike and his partner were called to the scene of an attempted armed robbery. During the ensuing gun battle, his partner was shot and killed. An investigation was held and the official findings hinted at the fact Mike might not have responded as he should have, had not come to the aid of his partner in a timely and professional manner. His courage was called into question, and although no formal action was taken, he suddenly put in for retirement. He never confided to his wife that he was resigning from the force, nor did he confer with her before selling their house on Twin Peaks and purchasing a retirement home in Palm Springs.

The first inkling Red had that her world was about to be turned upside down was the arrival of two men and a moving truck. She told the men, "There must be a mistake. You have the wrong address."

"Don't think so, lady." The man tapped a sheet of yellow paper. "Signed right here by Mike McGowan."

Red was furious, but if this was what he wanted, she would not stand in his way. While the men worked, she left the house, returning to find her home emptied of its contents. She sat cross-legged on the cold wood floor, in the middle of the living room, and cried. That was where Mike found her. He sat with her, and finally they began to talk. They talked more that evening than they had in years. When she asked why he had resigned from the police force he told her, "I just finally had enough."

"Enough of what?"

"The bullshit."

He told her he had purchased a home in Palm Springs and that they would be moving there. He said, "I want to get as far away from here as I can. I know I haven't always been fair and square with you, but I think we owe it to each other to give it one more shot. How about we start over? Maybe this time we can make each other happy."

They spent that night at a downtown hotel, and for the first time in an exceedingly long time they made love. Afterwards, he held her in his arms and told her he loved her. In the morning she was still nestled against his bare chest; his thick mat of chest hair tickled her nose but she did not complain. She wanted to lie there forever.

That day they drove south toward Los Angeles, and swung east on a narrow road. The countryside became steadily drier and the vegetation more sparse. Upon reaching the summit of the San Cabazon Gorgonia Pass, Mike pulled off the road at a viewpoint. From that vantage they could look across the floor of the broad valley and see the Little San Bernardino Mountains in the distance. Lined up in ascending rows, the peaks like pins in a bowling alley. Small white clouds were ironed onto the bright blue sky. Around them the air was alive, flecked with a glittering infusion of tiny, winged seeds flying on a swirling wind. As she drew a breath, the heat seemed to sear her lungs. She squinted at the harsh sunlight. A headache began to build behind her eyes.

Palm Springs was becoming a playground for the Hollywood stars, but in Red's estimation the town was little more than a dab of green floating on a sea of white shifting sand. They moved into a modest, flat-roofed adobe style house that wrapped around a small courtyard. She quickly fell into a routine of watering the flowers in the courtyard in the morning, napping during the heat of the day, and in late afternoon standing at the screen door and absently watching the vibrant colors of the sunsets fade into freckled silhouettes. At night she read romance books to help her fall asleep.

She tried to get Mike involved in activities—pleading with him to drive her to the mountains, take her out for dinner, go for walks—but he rarely did. He mostly just drank his Scotch and brooded.

Red was unwilling to be confined. She took long drives on the winding roads leading into the San Bernardino Mountains, went sightseeing at Joshua Tree National Park and shopped in out-of-the-way stores in the little bergs of Cathedral City, Palm Desert, Coachella, Yucca Valley and Twentynine Palms. Each time she returned home, Mike quizzed her, wanting to know every last detail about where she had been, what she had done and whom she had seen. She felt uncomfortable answering his countless probing questions. They did not sound like idle curiosity, but more like an interrogation.

Mike's personality underwent a relentless transformation. He became more and more unpleasant and disagreeable. One morning the telephone rang and Red was surprised to hear Helen's chipper voice. They had not spoken in several years. Helen said. "I heard you moved to Palm Springs. I'm going to

231

be spending the night just down the road in Indio and thought maybe we could get together for lunch."

‡‡‡‡‡‡‡

Red drove to Indio and found Helen. They went to a restaurant, and as soon as the waiter had taken their order, Helen reported the sad news, that Marge had recently passed away of congestive heart failure, and all the fine things she had accumulated during her lifetime had been sold at public auction to pay back taxes.

"I feel so badly," Red said as she unfolded the mauve cloth napkin and placed it precisely across her lap, using her hands to smooth down a few wayward wrinkles. "If I'd only known, I'd have come to the service. Guess after I got married, I lost touch with Marge. I just wasn't a very good friend, was I?"

Helen did not answer. She abruptly changed the subject, saying she had recently bought a trendy dress shop in Fremont. She talked about fashion, places in the city where she shopped and dined, and named some of the exciting and influential men she was dating. Red had little to offer. What could she talk about; her drunken husband, the caustic and trite events occurring inside the walls of their adobe home, the flowers in the courtyard she tended so religiously each day? She mainly just listened, and the more Helen talked, the more homesick she became for San Francisco and the vitality and diversity city life had to offer.

When Red arrived home she found Mike in an uncontrollable rage.

"Where the hell have you been? You've been gone for hours."

"I had lunch with a friend."

"A friend?"

"Yes, I still have friends."

He stood in front of her, arms folded across his brawny chest, so close Red could smell the stench of his boozy breath. She wished she had the strength to tell him their marriage was finished. She wanted to say she had had enough, was giving up, and would return to the city.

He stared at her, as if searching for a crack in the solid exterior she had built around herself. It was in that moment that he apparently came to a conclusion. He gulped the last of his drink, deliberately deposited the glass on the Formica tabletop and snatched up his wallet and checkbook.

"You and me are going uptown. We've got business to attend."

Mike told Red to drive. She wanted to know where to go. "Just drive." When they neared the Lincoln automobile dealership he directed, "Pull in here." He got out, leaned against a fender of a nearby car and waited. A well-dressed salesman approached. He told the man, "Mother needs a new car. How about that one over there?"

Mike bought a baby blue Lincoln convertible, trading in their old car. He wrote a check for the difference and handed the keys to Red. "All yours."

He was acting so strangely, so out of character that she did not know what to say, or what to expect next. She chose to just wait and see.

He glanced at his watch. "We're burning daylight. Drive me to the bank."

As they entered the bank, he took hold of her arm, gripping her elbow firmly and directing her to a teller's window. The young woman offered a cheery, "Good afternoon. How may I help the two of you?"

"I'm Mike McGowan. Find out how much I've got in my savings account."

The teller closed the small double-doors to her window and was gone several minutes. She returned, reopened the doors and handed him a slip of paper on which she had written *$30,027.94.*

He removed his checkbook, did some figuring on a blank page and wrote a check for $15,013.97. He handed it to the teller, directing, "Cash this."

"I'll have to have Mr. Peterson's authorization."

The teller returned with a middle-aged man dressed in charcoal slacks, white shirt and a green tie. He was holding the check between his thumb and forefinger. "You wish to cash this?"

"That's the general idea."

"This is for a significant amount of money."

"I know. I wrote it."

"Are you sure you want that much cash?"

"I want it now."

"Yes, sir."

Crisp bills were counted and tucked inside a green bank bag. When the transaction was completed, he took the bag and shoved it at Red. "There you go. Half of what I got. I'm leaving you."

Her voice was thin, a frightened whimper. "Where are you going?"

He was walking away, but paused, turned slowly, and then his voice boomed across the quiet room. "I don't know where the hell I'm going, but I guarantee it'll be far enough away that if you send me a postcard it'll cost you nine bucks postage."

She drove the Lincoln home. The green bank bag sat benignly on the white leather seat beside her. She firmly believed Mike's anger would dissipate; he would come to his senses and return home. But when dawn dragged with it the certainty of a new day, she picked up the telephone and called the motel in Indio, asking for Helen's room.

"Hello."

"I'm so glad I caught you before you left."

Helen could tell something was wrong. When she asked, Red responded with a sob, "It's Mike. He went crazy."

"Did he hit you?"

"No, nothing like that. He left me."

"I can be there in an hour."

"No, I'll drive over there."

Red drove the blue Lincoln with the top down, her red hair blowing wildly in the wind. She had presence of mind to run a brush through her unruly hair before going from the dazzling sunlight into the darkened motel room. Once inside she sat on the bed and sobbed into a beige towel, pouring forth the sordid details of her regrettable marriage.

"It's finished. Kaput. Over and done. Dead." She gave a sniffle, then gritted her teeth and toughened her resolve. "That rotten son of a bitch." She felt better for having said that, stronger and more determined. "If he hadn't done it, I was going to. The good thing is, he bought me the new car and gave me half his money. I didn't have to fight him."

Helen had been fixing a pair of drinks in motel glasses. She paused and asked, "How much?" Red told her the number. "So, what are you going to do with it?"

"Don't know. Haven't had time to even give it a thought. Live on it I suppose. What should I do? I guess I better open a savings account."

"That's no good. You have to make your money work for you. Use it to start a brand new life."

"I guess I could open a business." Red was thinking about a dress shop. "But I don't know anything about business."

"It isn't hard." Helen took a sip from her glass. "Indulge me a moment. If you could be anyone in the whole wide world, who would you be?"

Red tilted her head in thought and concluded, "I guess I'd want to be Marge when she owned the big house in the Tenderloin."

"Why in heaven's name Marge?"

"Lots of reasons. It always seemed to me she made that big house a home and everyone who stepped through the door was part of one big happy family. She was fun-loving, sociable, made a good living and gave back to the community. It would be nice to be able to help some deserving person like she helped me."

Helen burst into laughter.

"Did I say something wrong?"

"No, not at all." Helen's laughter died away. "I was just remembering the time I caught you peeking around the corner, watching the ladies take their customers upstairs. You were so young and naïve. You asked if we were chippies." They laughed together.

"I'll let you in on a little secret," Red said. "I asked her for a job."

"And Marge turned you down on the spot, didn't she?"

"Yes, but I never understood why. I guess I wasn't pretty enough."

"Never think that. Marge saw something more in you. She told me you were like a precious little flower, and that when the right young man came along, he'd make you bloom. She said you had too much potential to waste."

"She said that?"

"She certainly did."

Helen poured more bourbon in the glasses. Red took a sip. "Marge did a lot of good in her life. She made the world a more civilized place."

"Tell me something, if there was an opportunity for you to go into that business, have your own place, would you be interested?"

"I don't know. I've never considered...."

Helen clapped her hands together. "It just so happens I'm planning to look into the possibility of buying a place in Winnemucca, Nevada. The Red Lantern is up for sale, and from what I've been told, it's a can't miss moneymaker."

"Nevada?"

"Brothels are legal in some counties in Nevada, just as legal as owning a dress shop. The main thing is we need to act fast, before someone else snaps it up. What do you think?"

"I don't know. What do you think?"

"I think we go in as partners, you and me. We just jump in with both feet."

Before Red had an opportunity to respond, Helen had already picked up the telephone and was making a call. From that moment forward, everything fell into place so quickly and with such ease, Red concluded it had to be fate.

Helen returned the phone to the cradle and gushed, "It's a done deal. We'll use some of your money for the down payment. Our place will be outrageously extravagant, flimflam from floor to ceiling. But you have to know, our success hinges on the girls we choose. Doves make or break a joint."

"How will it work?"

"We'll split it down the middle, 50-50. Once we open, I'll line up the girls and you run the business. Easy as pie."

That evening Red could not sleep. She longed for Mike to step from the shadows, but he did not come to reclaim her heart. Morning sunlight slowly crept up the patterned folds of the curtains. The night air began to warm. A fly awakened and beat against the windowpane in a futile and frenzied attempt to gain its freedom. She opened the window and set it free.

Chapter Seventeen

Nellie, pregnant and big bellied, recognized her brother straight away. Her eyes widened and she let out a high-pitched squeal as she stepped over the threshold and flung her arms around Jack. "What a wonderful surprise. I can't believe it's you, finally, after all these years."

Once inside, Nellie motioned toward a toddler on the floor, playing with wooden blocks. "That's Jimmy." To her son she said, "This is your Uncle Jack. Remember, I told you about Uncle Jack?"

Jack held out his hands and the boy got up off the floor and came waddling to him. He threw his arms around Jack's neck and squeezed.

"You're hurting me," Jack kidded. When the boy began squirming, Jack returned him to the floor. He scampered away and returned to his blocks.

"I stopped downtown and saw Kelsey. He told me where you lived and what happened. I can't even begin to imagine... things must have been pretty tough. You know, Sis, I'm real sorry. There were a hundred times I started home, but I always found an excuse. I was wrong for not coming back."

239

"There wasn't anything you could have done. After that night you stood up to him...anyway, he never raised his hand to Momma again. Say, Momma gave me something. She said when you came back I was supposed to give it to you. I'll get it."

With a groan, she pushed her bulk from the chair and stood. She went into her bedroom and returned a moment later with a handcrafted wooden box, the corners intricately dovetailed, brass hinges on the lid. She sat down beside Jack, opened the lid, and brought out a stack of envelopes tied with a faded red ribbon.

"Momma kept each and every letter you ever sent. I think she treasured them more than anything. It broke her heart she could never write back."

He fanned out the envelopes, recognizing the postmarks: Standing Rock, New Mexico; Globe, Arizona; Pine Valley, California; Yuma, Arizona; El Paso, Texas; Torreon, Mexico; Ciudad Madero, Mexico; Liberty, Texas. Each town held a multitude of memories for Jack like snapshots of his life. A life lived constantly on the move. This was tangible proof of his mother's love. She had always loved him. Jack realized, on every mile of his journey, she must have been his guardian angel, protecting him as best she could.

Nellie announced, "You're staying with us. Ted will be so happy to finally meet you. He'll be home any time now. The two of you will get along famously. I'll make up the spare bed in Little Jack's room. Where are your bags?"

Jack shook his head. "What you see, is all I got." He returned the letters to the box.

The following morning he hiked uptown, bought a new shirt at the clothing store, put it on in the dressing room, and went directly from there to the boarding house Nellie had recommended and took a room.

The *News Tribune*, located only a short block from the boarding house, was a substantial brick building. The front portion was devoted to offices and the back housed the production department and printing presses. Jack opened the door and could hear the rattle and clack of the press. The building seemed to vibrate like a locomotive running down an uneven track. He smelled ink, grease and cigar smoke. The receptionist, an older lady with silver hair, inquired without looking up, "May I help you?"

"Yes, ma'am. I'd like to see Mr. Soodel."

"And you are?"

"Jack Small. But Mr. Soodel isn't expecting me."

The receptionist looked up. "He most certainly is, in fact, he mentioned he wanted to see you the minute you arrived." She stood. "Please follow me."

The receptionist led him on a winding course between desks, several of which appeared to be unoccupied, and ushered him to the door of the editor's office. Inside, seated behind an undersized desk piled high with papers, was a very large man wearing gray wool slacks, a wrinkled white shirt and black suspenders. He looked like a caricature of what an editor should look like. He was oblivious to all but the story he was working on, hunting and pecking at the keys of an ancient standup Underwood typewriter, using only his two index fingers. The stub of a fat cigar protruded from one corner of his mouth.

The woman tapped politely on the open door. "Sir, Mr. Small has arrived."

"Well, Jesus tap-dancing Christ, come on in." Fred Soodel removed the cigar from his mouth and jumped to his feet. The two men shook hands.

"About goddamned time you got here." Fred motioned with his cigar toward a chair. "Have a seat. Kelsey talked to me yesterday. He's my best advertiser. Gives you a pretty goddamn high recommendation, he does. From what he says, the two of you had one hell of an adventure, back when you were kids. So tell me about your experience as a reporter? Where've you worked?"

"I'm going to level with you, Mr. Soodel."

"Please do. Call me Fred."

"My only newspaper work was with the *Folsom Gazette*." Jack watched one of Fred's bushy eyebrows arch upward. He went on, "I served my time. Now I want to try to be a newspaper man. It might interest you to know I received an award from the Northern California Newspaper Association for the best feature of the year."

"And I'll be equally forthright with you, Mr. Small. This is my situation: the war is in full swing, there's a manpower shortage and I'm desperate for good reporters. I've got women writing recipes for the cooking page, women writing obits, women writing features about Aunt Tillie's doll collection and Uncle Henry's prize Jersey giving birth to triplets. I got women running out my ears. What I need is a hard news man. Someone to sniff out a story, dig down, uncover the facts and write it up with words that bite you like a rabid dog chewing on a lamb's leg. That's the kind of man I need, Mr. Small.

"Just so you know, I've never hired a convict in my life, but desperate times require desperate measures. Kelsey says you're trustworthy and hard-working. Make goddamn sure you are."

Jack sat a little straighter. "You mean I have the job?"

Fred nodded.

"When do I start?"

"Right now. Take the desk outside my door. Pay is nine bucks a week. Now quit wasting time and get to work."

Jack got lucky. His first story was going to be an update about the naval ammunition depot north of town. He was at the site, gathering background information, when one of the silos exploded, killing three men. The concussion from the blast was heard and felt 20 miles away in Grand Island. Jack's story, byline and photographs of smoking ruins, was picked up by the AP wire service and ran in nearly every daily newspaper in the country, as well as some foreign newspapers. On payday Jack discovered his salary had been increased by $3 a week.

┣┅┅┅┅┅┅┫

Jack called for an interview when the City of Hastings hired a new recreation director, Kay Nicholson. He planned to write a story about the upcoming baseball tryouts. As he approached the open office door of the Recreation Department, he found a young lady bent over at the waist pulling books from a box. He stood in the entryway admiring the way the skirt molded itself to her shapely backside.

Kay must have sensed him there. She abruptly straightened and turned toward the door. She had blond hair that curled around her pretty face. Her skin was pink with light brown freckles randomly scattered across her cheeks and over her nose.

Jack cleared his throat, stated his name and mentioned the newspaper. She slapped her hands together as if they were dusty, took a step in Jack's direction and extended her right hand. "Kay Nicholson. Nice to meet you, Jack Small, *News Tribune.*

"So, you want to know about baseball tryouts. Since this is my first day on the job, I don't have all the facts, but I'll answer the best I can. What I don't know, I'll either fake, or find out." She laughed and motioned for Jack to have a seat on the bench. She sat beside him, lifting the hem of her dress a little and crossing her leg, one over the other. He opened his notepad and pulled a pencil from behind his ear. He began his interview by asking when the tryouts were scheduled and followed that with a series of questions: who could try out, how many teams would be chosen, and the time and location of the tryouts? When he ran out of questions he closed his notepad, and screwing up his courage. "Would you consider going to dinner with me tonight?"

"I'd very much like to have dinner with you, but rather than have you spend your hard-earned money, what say you come over to my place? I love to cook."

"What can I bring?"

"Just yourself and maybe a bottle of champagne. We'll celebrate."

┼┼┼┼┼┼┼

Kay, wearing a loose-fitting, colorful print dress, met Jack at the door. She took his arm and led him inside. He handed her the bottle of champagne.

"I'll put it in the refrigerator so it will be nice and cold."

Jack breathed in an intoxicating blend of her perfume and the pot roast cooking in the oven. He remained standing, watching as she moved efficiently around the kitchen. The oil furnace kicked on and the house seemed to lurch a little.

"What do you think?" Kay asked.

"You, you look pretty."

"Not me, silly, the house. Didn't the landlord do a bang-up job? When I visited a month ago, I talked him into repainting the kitchen and laying new linoleum."

"Real cozy. Is there anything I can do to help?"

244

"You could set the table if you like." She pointed toward the utensil drawer. While he laid out the silverware, plates and napkins, she set a pair of red candles, thin and tapered, on the table and lit them. She turned off the lights, and the room was filled with a warm, romantic glow.

After they finished eating, the dishes were piled in the sink. Kay insisted they could be washed later, and suggested they retire to the living room. She opened the champagne and brought two glasses and the bottle into the room. She went to the phonograph and turned it on. Duke Ellington orchestra purred softly. She sat beside Jack, poured champagne into the glasses and proposed a toast.

"To us."

She touched the rim of her glass to his and he was acutely aware of the softness of her breasts where she leaned against him. He watched as she sipped and then licked her upper lip. Then she became abruptly somber.

"I'm a firm believer in honesty, having everything out in the open. I think you should know that technically I'm still married, but we're in the process of having that terrible mistake annulled. It would already be over and done with but Rick, that's his name, was sent to Hanford, Washington, to work on some top secret war project."

"You're married, but you're not going to be?"

"Just as soon as he gets leave, it'll be taken care of once and for all. Just a formality. And you, ever been married?"

"Nope."

"Been close? Engaged?"

"No on both counts."

"A good-looking fellow like you, now that's hard to believe."

Most of the champagne was gone when Kay set her glass on the coffee table, reached and took his glass and placed it next to hers. She leaned into him and kissed him. The kiss began as an innocent brushing of lips and ended as a hungry grinding of unrepressed passion.

To Jack it seemed as if one moment they were contently sitting on the sofa, just talking, and the next they were in bed and had already made love. He had absolutely no recollection of undressing, removing his prosthesis, or anything leading up to the stupendous event. Kay was now nestled against his chest, running a long, pink fingernail over the tattoo on his stomach. "How did you get this?"

He told her about his days as a hobo, saying he got the tattoo when he was in jail for trespassing on railroad property, and that the tattoo, *Nevada Kid,* was a name he fought under when he was a boxer. She wanted to know about the accident that cost him his leg, and when he told her she asked, "Does it still bother you?"

"I'm used to it."

She abruptly interrupted him by biting his neck—a playful bite—then she licked his earlobe and worked her way downward to one nipple and then the other. They made love again.

Dawn was beginning to bring a soft hue to a new day when Jack kissed Kay and departed. He walked to the boarding house, took a quick bath, got into his clothes, and was five minutes early for the city budget meeting. A few hours later, when he arrived at the newspaper office, the receptionist handed him an envelope. He went to his desk to open it.

Dearest Jack,

I'm sorry I can't talk to you in person and explain things, but by the time you read this letter I will be gone.

Not long after you left, my husband came home and surprised me. He wants to make a fresh start. We are moving to Denver and will be living with my parents, at least for a while, until we get a place of our own.

Sorry for the way things turned out because I really did care for you. Don't feel sad. I know another girl will come along and you will marry her, have a family and live happily ever after.

I'll always remember the one special night we shared.

Forever yours,

Kay

Over the course of the next several days Jack tried to compose a response. He wrote several letters, but threw them all away. Finally, exasperated, he scribbled words on paper and mailed it to the address Kay had written on the envelope.

Dear Kay,

You enclosed your return address in Denver so I figured you wouldn't mind if I sent you a short note. I hope you are healthy and happy. I read your letter, and even tried to read between the lines, but I still don't know what to think. I guess sometimes things just aren't meant to make sense.

I don't know what else to write except I miss you.

Jack

⋮⋮⋮⋮⋮⋮⋮

Jack,

Why are you bothering me? I wrote you goodbye. That was supposed to be the end of it. Your letter writing is interfering with my marriage. Rick is jealous and very suspicious. Please don't write and cause me any more grief.

Kay

‡‡‡‡‡‡‡

After receiving her note, Jack believed his fling with Kay was over and done with, and then one afternoon the receptionist let Jack know he had a telephone call.

"This is Jack."

"Hello Jack."

He recognized Kay's voice immediately.

"Jack, if you have any feelings for me, you'll come save me."

"From what? Where are you?"

"Denver. You have my address."

"Where's your husband?

"Gone. Good riddance to him. Are you coming?"

"I don't know. Let me see what I can do."

After the phone call ended, Jack tried to go back to the story he was writing, but he could not concentrate and ducked around the corner to the Buffalo Lounge where he sat in a secluded corner, drinking beer, smoking cigarettes and trying to investigate exactly what he was feeling. He tipped his beer and felt the way the cool liquid coated his dry throat, allowing himself to be enveloped in a warm cocoon of bar light filtered through cigarette haze, and buffeted by the gyrating noises of glasses tapping the bar, soft music and muted conversations.

‡‡‡‡‡‡‡

When Kay did not hear from Jack, she placed a racy photograph in a manila folder and mailed it to him at the *News Tribune*. The large envelope was dropped on Jack's desk and he opened it, but upon catching a glimpse of the image he placed the envelope in his open desk drawer and slowly removed the glossy photograph paper. Kay was naked, propped up on her elbows. The smooth curves of her breasts, as well as her round bottom were visible.

"Damn it."

He shoved the photograph inside the envelope, got up from his chair and went directly to Fred Soodel's office.

"I need to take a few days off."

"It's not trouble with the law is it?"

"No, sir, a personal matter."

Fred gave a knowing grin and leaned back in his chair. "Must be a dame. Go if you must, but make damn sure you come back. I don't know what I'd do without you."

⌗⌗⌗⌗⌗⌗

When Jack arrived, Kay threw herself into his arms and promptly crammed his seven-year-old pea green Dodge sedan with her belongings. They drove east. At a motel near Fort Morgan they got a room and made love. He asked her to marry him. She refused, saying she would never marry again, but promised to live with him and be his common-law wife. Jack had no choice but to settle for her any way he could get her.

Kay was able to reclaim her job with the City of Hastings, and for several years she lived with Jack. It was never a fairytale romance; sometimes they coexisted and simply endured the cold snaps, other times he moved out and took a room for a month or two, until they could patch up their differences.

⌗⌗⌗⌗⌗⌗

Kay announced she had taken a job on the West Coast. She packed up and moved to Salem, Oregon, where she worked with Children's Services in an office complex overlooking the capitol building and the golden logger that graced the top of the rotunda.

A few weeks later, Jack gave notice at the *News Tribune* and followed her to Oregon. He found employment as a reporter for the *Capital Press*. Once again they lived together, but it was not long before she drove him away. She was good at that,

249

driving him away, and then as she always did, she pulled him back when she needed him.

The constant conflicts between the two had a strange quality of sameness, very contrived and predictably orchestrated. Leading up to each separation, Kay became moody and withdrawn. Jack escaped, tossing his camping gear in the back of his Hudson sedan and disappearing. He might go to Nevada, Montana, Wyoming, Washington, or up to Idaho's panhandle. He could be gone for weeks or months. While he was away he dug placer gold from one of his many mining claims scattered around the country. Other times he worked at small town newspapers. Eventually he always returned to Kay.

Jack turned to alcohol to help mask his pain. He was drinking the night he wrecked the Hudson, plowing the substantial car with thick steel and a lot of weight, into an elm tree less than a quarter-mile from the rural home near Salem that he shared with Kay. She heard the crash, dashed up the road with flashlight in hand, saw steam venting from the busted radiator, mistook it for smoke and thinking the car had caught fire, she screamed at him to get out. He locked the doors.

She picked up a broken limb and bashed out the windshield. He never moved, never flinched, just sat there motionless. She finally gave up and went home.

The following morning he wandered into the kitchen with dried blood on his face, and took a seat at the table. She served him sausage and eggs, sunny side up, just the way he liked them.

Chapter Eighteen

The coming of the railroad in the 1868 gave birth to the town of Winnemucca, Nevada, located roughly at the midway point between Salt Lake City and San Francisco. A stockyard was built adjacent to the siding and served as the terminus for cattle drives from across the High Desert region. To accommodate the needs of the cowboys, and the miners who came to separate gold from the shifting sand, a district of legal brothels was created a few blocks from the center of town. But the boom times had long since passed and the district had deteriorated to a sad collection of dilapidated shacks.

Red parked her Lincoln in front of the Red Lantern, rolled down the window and stared dejectedly at the building. It was little more than a festering sore with boarded up windows and a sagging front porch that threatened to give way and collapse at any moment. At Helen's urging, Red had plunked down $5,000 as a down payment to buy the building. Then Helen backed out of their partnership, saying she needed to devote her time and resources to her dress shop in Fremont, and besides, Winnemucca was just too far away.

Red sat in her baby blue convertible and acknowledged the obvious, that if anyone was going to make a go of the Red Lantern it rested solely upon her shoulders. Her dilemma was that on one hand she did not want to squander her investment, and on the other, common sense dictated she cut her losses, make a quick U-turn and leave immediately.

An old man, pulled by a dog on a leash, approached the Lincoln. When he drew near he glanced toward the car, and seeing the melancholy look on Red's face he inquired, "You okay, honey?"

Red did not respond. The old man looked where she was looking, took note of the dilapidated building and remarked, "She went tits up 'cause they had ugly women. Hell, a man can go home if he wants to see an ugly woman." The dog tugged impatiently at the leash. "Well, sister, you take care."

Red watched the man and the dog move to the corner, where the dog sniffed a post, lifted his hind leg and dutifully squirted. Red returned her attention to the building, seeing it for the eyesore it was, but also recognizing that it did have potential.

"It'll take a lot of work, and money too. I'm already in so deep I can't back out, not now."

She hired a Mexican man and his son to remove the porch and tear down the walls to bare studs. A crew from Twin Falls, Idaho, put up board-and-batten siding, which they painted with red stain. The interior was refurbished: the electrical and plumbing updated, sheetrock hung, a hardwood floor installed, a new ceiling added and all the windows replaced. She oversaw every last detail.

When her money ran low, she stopped at the Silver State Bank and asked the branch manager if she could take him to lunch. After they had eaten, she drove past the Red Lantern and showed the banker how the remodel was progressing. She explained her vision. The Red Lantern was to rival the finest establishments in San Francisco, only on a much smaller scale. On the spot, the banker gave her a $10,000 line of credit. He told her if she needed more, to come back and see him.

Red spared no expense creating a small parlor that served as the showpiece of the house. The room was decorated with Persian rugs, brocade love seats and settees, leather chairs, red velvet curtains, a dazzling beveled-glass chandelier and a fancy bar. As the work progressed, and the building became more and more attractive, working girls from as far away as Las Vegas dropped by to tell Red, when she got ready to hire, to keep them in mind. She dutifully took down their names and contact information.

The day before the Red Lantern's scheduled grand opening, the first Friday in October, a powerful storm roared in off the Pacific Ocean. The Sierra Nevada Mountains tore open the underbellies of the moisture-laden clouds. On the broad sweep of the High Desert, a gusty wind blew summer's dust around until a hard-slicing rain arrived to settle it. It was the type of fall storm that sends field mice burrowing, forces other wild creatures to take refuge in their nests and lairs, and causes geese to pull out and continue their southern migration.

Red lay in her bed restlessly listening to the chaos occurring outside her backroom apartment. At times, when the wind and rain eased, she could hear flocks of Canada geese passing noisily overhead. They told all who would listen about the splendid season they had spent above the Arctic Circle, and how much they were looking forward to following summer south. She envied the birds their freedom to roam and worried the storm would disrupt her grand opening.

By morning, all that remained of the storm were broken shards of clouds scurrying eastward over the head of a solitary buckaroo. He rode through the chill of the High Desert air; his horse weaving between clumps of gray-green sage while a pronghorn stood on a rise, serving as sentry to the band feeding below in the valley. The sentry watched the man and his horse pass slowly from sight. A lone magpie, like a driven needle, traversed the quilted sky. A rattlesnake crawled from beneath a boulder and ribboned its way up the rock to lie on a flat spot and steal some of the building warmth.

He breathed in the sweet tang of sage and savored the humid smells of wet earth that ripen the desert air all too infrequently. He sensed mustangs out there roaming the landscape, and although he looked intently for them, he never saw any sign of wild horses on the move. He was planning to get his work done early, then make a run to Winnemucca in the afternoon and be on hand for the grand opening of the Red Lantern. A friend had told him some fine looking out-of-town ladies had been imported for the occasion. He sure as hell was not going to miss a chance at new blood and the fun that went along with it.

┆┄┆┄┆┄┆

The custom of the red lantern originated in Dodge City, Kansas, when railroaders left their red lanterns hanging outside the whorehouse doors to discourage intruders. When the special hour for the grand opening of the Red Lantern was at hand, Red flipped the switch and the red lantern glowed in neon. The crowd of men who were gathered outside cheered lustily.

Buckaroos, miners, railroaders, a barber, a banker, a few traveling salesmen, and even a schoolteacher from Golconda stepped across the threshold of the Red Lantern. Red was there to greet each arriving guest. She introduced herself and asked the customer's first name, escorted him to the parlor and seated him at the bar. After the man had been served a drink, and if he was in the mood, he let his intentions be known. Red rang a small silver bell and available ladies, dressed in an array of revealing negligees, appeared for the customer's inspection.

Six ladies were working the grand opening, as well as a maid to pick up towels and change sheets between customers. A bouncer had been hired just in case of trouble. With only five rooms available, Red had to juggle the girls and the guests. One of the guests misplaced his shirt and returned to the parlor wearing pants and suspenders over a white T-shirt. He was a rough looking fellow with pale arms and sun-blackened hands. His battered ball cap was shoved way back on his head. He tossed down a straight shot of Johnny Walker Red Label and chased it quickly with a beer.

"I don't want no more girls. I want me a full-blowed woman." He made a clumsy grab for Red. "I want you."

She was faster than the drunken man, and skillfully moved away and ducked behind the protection of the bar.

"I'm not for sale."

"Everything has its price. Name it. I'm gonna buy you."

Red had the bouncer get rid of the man, but later, after she had time to reflect, she realized if she had simply brought one of the girls to sit with the man, flirt and tease him, he probably would have spent another 20 or 30 bucks.

Red seemed to have been born with the ability to run a business that involved socializing with men, but she soon discovered a hidden talent—a flamboyant side to her personality—that made her a convincing actress. She could play whatever role was required: the coarse sexuality of Mae West, the fun-loving tease of Claudette Colbert, the scandalous sensuality of Clara Bow. She gave each guest what it was he desired most while renting out her company's assets.

Knowing contented customers would talk to their friends about the plush surroundings, the accommodating hostess and the beautiful and talented ladies of her establishment, Red employed paid advertising in the form of *cappers*. The cappers were men who visited local bars and distributed business cards on which was printed the name and address of the Red Lantern, as well as the discreet message, *MORE THAN JUST THE COMFORTS OF HOME*. If a capper ran into a potential customer who was planning on being in town for a spell, but was hesitant about visiting a brothel, the capper handed out a wooden nickel. On one side was featured a red lantern and on the reverse side was stamped, *GOOD FOR A FREE ONE*.

The pain in her abdomen and lower back came on without warning, and so completely incapacitated Red that she had to be driven to the emergency room. The attending physician, after his examination and blood and urine tests, informed her she was attempting to pass a kidney stone.

"What happens now?"

"We wait and hope you pass it."

"How long does that usually take?"

"Sometimes an hour. Sometimes a number of days."

"I can't afford this. I have a business to run."

"Better make arrangements to have someone run it for you. I'm keeping you in the hospital."

The only person Red could think of whom she could trust, and who had the ability to run the business in her absence, was Helen. She placed a call to Helen, informed her of the situation, and asked her to catch the next train to Winnemucca.

To her credit, Helen dropped everything and came, bringing along several friends, sporting ladies all. They proceeded to parade up and down the main street of Winnemucca in Red's Lincoln Continental convertible. With the top down, the ladies sat up high on the deck, boldly exhibiting their wares. They kicked up their legs, showing off stockings and garters and glimpses of creamy flesh. As if that public display was not bold enough, Helen went one step further, by inviting the prominent townsmen to a *soiree*.

Business leaders, ranchers, mine owners, government officials, legislators, lawmen and judges attended the gala event. They dined on fresh oysters, squid, caviar and other delicacies imported from the coast on a bed of ice. Liquor flowed freely and the girls were kept busy demonstrating their wide range of erotic talents for the benefit of their enthusiastic guests.

The climax to Helen's short stint as the Red Lantern's madam came the following evening when she and her bevy of girls sashayed into a packed council meeting. Helen proceeded to the front of the room.

"Mayor, councilmen, chief, and many of you from the audience, too. We would like to express our sincere gratitude and deepest appreciation for your patronage at the Red Lantern last evening. We had quite a time, didn't we?" Helen chucked the mayor under his chin, winked suggestively at the city attorney, and blew a hot kiss to the chief of police.

A reporter from the *Humboldt Sun* newspaper was in attendance at the meeting. He failed to print even one word of the unusual proceedings, but told a friend, "It was so quiet in that council chambers you could have heard a mouse fart, and then this out-of-town hussy offers to make a tribute payment. The mayor says he doesn't have any idea what she's talking about. She proceeds to tell him paying for sin is the custom in

San Francisco. She says she assumes Winnemucca runs the same type of show.

"The chief of police, his face as red as a thermometer about to explode, informs this woman Winnemucca is most certainly not San Francisco. He orders the harlots escorted from the chamber, but the damage has been done. The whole damn town suddenly knows what went on, and I guarantee every man started preparing his alibi to protect himself when he walked in the house and his wife asked, 'Were you at the Red Lantern last night?'"

⊢⊣⊢⊣⊢⊣

While Red remained confined to her hospital bed, where she painfully passed a kidney stone, in a closed-door session, the Winnemucca City Council voted to jerk the Red Lantern's business license. Just like that, the grandest whorehouse east of San Francisco passed into the scandalous history of the town.

Without a license to operate, Red was forced to sell the Red Lantern, absorb the loss, and move on. She traveled 120 miles east to Elko, Nevada, a town that clung equally to the open range and the mainline of the Southern Pacific. Trains carrying soldiers toward the front line in the Philippines and the South Pacific passed that way. The local cowboys hardly took notice of the coming and going of the soldiers. They continued to go about their routine of riding horses across the open range and driving pickup trucks with steel posts and rolls of barbed wire rattling around in the back. They set the posts into the arid ground and strung wire in an arrogant battle to delineate boundaries.

Red took a job waiting tables at the Overland Café, where the cowboys came and went, as did the soldiers who hiked up from the station when the trains stopped to take on coal and water. She felt sad for the men in uniform and tried to imagine which of them were destined to die on foreign soil, leaving behind girlfriends, wives and families. All that long winter the men came in stomping their boots, sloughing off coats and head gear, reversing the process on their way out.

Red moved between tables wearing comfortable shoes— the type nurses wear—a practical skirt and a loose fitting blouse. She carried herself with that certain weariness that defeat seems to bring, moving with efficiency, pulling 10-hour shifts. Usually she had a distant cast to her eyes, as if looking at something in the distant past, or hoping the future might be brighter on the far horizon. She had put on a few extra pounds that tended to soften her features. She was no longer as attractive as she had once been.

Living in Elko was an isolated and lonely existence. Red had little time and not much energy for adventure or romance. For a while she dated a rancher from Oregon, but after a week together he admitted he was married. Then there was the handsome cattle buyer from Chicago. She took a liking to him, but he returned to Chicago and never called her again. The last man she had been with was a sergeant in the U.S. Army. He was from Philadelphia and had bushy eyebrows as dark as unsweetened chocolate. She took him to bed, not out of passion, but mostly out of compassion. She had a strong feeling he would not be coming home from overseas and treated him to a night he would long remember. Over the course of the next six or seven months he wrote her more than a dozen letters. In the last letter he mentioned his unit was being sent to Iwo Jima. There had been no further communication from him and she feared the worst. It seemed to her, every man she chose was the wrong man. She wondered if that was her lot in life and if maybe she should just quit choosing.

One afternoon, after the lunch crowd had dispersed, Red stepped to a table where a local rancher, an older man who never removed his cowboy hat, not even when he was eating, and a kid he had just hired to work for him, were sitting. The kid ordered a cup of barley soup and asked for extra crackers. The old rancher said, "I'm buying. You best have more than a bowl of soup 'cause we got a ton of work to do and it's gonna be a long time 'fore dinner."

The kid changed his order to a cheeseburger basket. The rancher wanted chicken fried steak. Red asked if he wanted fries or mashed with that, and green beans or corn. The rancher wanted mashed and green beans.

"You get carrot Jell-O salad with that, too."

The rancher nodded his approval.

The phone, hanging on the wall between the dining room and the kitchen, rang loudly. Red started to move in that direction, was going to answer it, but the rancher stopped her by asking, "Say, does that chicken fried steak come with gravy?"

"You know just as well as I do, it comes with gravy."

"Suppose you could ladle a little on the spuds?"

"I don't do it myself. I'll ask the cook. He's an independent cuss; you never know."

"See what you can do about the gravy."

The cook had answered the phone and he extended it in Red's direction.

Red underlined "extra gravy" twice and handed the order to the cook. She took the phone. "Hello."

"Hello back at you." The voice was vaguely familiar, but she could not place it right off. The voice said, "Princess, you ever get around to divorcing me?"

Now she knew that voice—Mike.

"No. But I hope to hell you did."

"Wouldn't look good for a man to divorce a lady. Guess we're still husband and wife."

260

"Ain't that about like a poke in the eye with a sharp stick?"

"Don't make it sound all that bad. Heard you had a *business* in Winnemucca, but lost it."

"Who told you that?"

"Word gets around. They claimed it was a nice place, but now I hear you're dealing off the wing."

"Meaning what?"

"Waiting tables."

"Girl's got to live."

"How about coming to San Francisco? We could spend a few days getting reacquainted."

"Don't think so. I knew you once. Once was plenty."

"It might interest you that I gave up drinking. You know, booze is a funny thing. It can make you feel 10 feet tall or make you feel awful damn small. When I started feeling small, I quit."

The cook rang his bell, trying to get Red's attention and let her know her order was up.

"I've got to get back to work."

"What I did to you wasn't right. Here lately it's been eating at me. Let me make it up to you. I want to apologize in person. At least give me that."

Red began to feel something, maybe sympathy or even a touch of tenderness, whatever it was she attempted to hide it. "I remember you said you were going so far away it'd cost me nine bucks to send you a postcard."

"I've been there, but now I'm home. Come on, why don't you spend a weekend with me? Be like when we were first together. Remember? We had some good times."

"Easy for you to say."

"I'll take you shopping."

The cook rang his bell again, this time with more urgency, and called, "Order up!" The rancher and the kid were looking at Red. She eased around the corner with the phone so she would be out of the line of sight from the dining room.

"Wire me the money for a train ticket. Send it here to the Overland Cafe. I'll think about it."

▞▞▞▞▞▞

Red found that seeing Mike again after all the time that had passed, was a pleasant surprise. His brown eyes shone with merriment that reflected all the foreign ports of call he had visited as a merchant seaman. He looked fit, tan, and was every bit the handsome and dashing man she had run into on the sidewalk so many years before. The most noticeable difference was his mustache, now speckled and his dark hair turning silver at the temples, giving him an almost distinguished appearance.

At dinner they were seated across from each other at a table in a small seafood restaurant on Fisherman's Wharf.

"You still care about me, don't you?" he asked.

"I care about a lot of people."

"The war is winding down and when it's over I want to show you the world—Tahiti, New Zealand, South America...."

"Not interested."

"Don't be heartless. Allow me the opportunity to make it up to you."

"You've already apologized for leaving the way you did. That's plenty."

"What will it take for you to actually forgive me, to see I've got my feet on the ground and I'm not the man I used to be?"

She gazed off across the bay, to where a tug was pushing a barge around.

"Let me put it this way. You're the only woman I could ever trust. I don't want to live out my days a lonely old man. I want you to be with me. If I can't have you all the time, I'm willing

262

to settle for you part time. You tell me, what do I have to do? What do you want?"

"I don't want anything."

"Answer this—tell me a time in your life when you were the most satisfied, the happiest?"

Red knew he wanted her to say her best days were when they were first married and living on Twin Peaks, but she refused to give him the satisfaction.

"When I owned the Red Lantern."

"I've got plenty of money. You pick any town you want and I'll build you a new place. You run it, have fun, enjoy yourself, keep the money and visit me when you can. What do you think about an arrangement like that?"

Red visualized herself as a haggard old woman waiting tables at the Overland. She saw the faces of her customers: the vacant stares of the soldiers, the devilish grins of the truck drivers who tried to slap her bottom each time she passed, the pompous businessmen who stopped talking when she poured their coffee. How could she face a lifetime of that, especially when Mike was willing to bankroll her? And yet she knew she no longer loved Mike, and if she accepted his offer it was only a slightly different form, but surely equivalent to, the act of prostitution.

"I want to stay in Nevada where it's legal."

"Fine."

"I'll be the one who decides when and where we get together. This arrangement will be on my terms."

"I'm at sea a lot. I'll let you know when I'm coming in. If we can spend time together, fine and dandy. No hooks in anybody's ass. Red, you're going to be my precious little flower all over again, aren't you?"

"In case you haven't noticed, the bloom's fading fast."

Red instructed her attorney to write up an offer on a small ranch bordering Highway 228. She applied to Elko County and was granted the necessary permits, and when she called and told Mike the cost, he promptly wired the funds to buy the land, pay the fees and complete the building project.

The setting for what was to become *Red's Place* was out in the country, 20 miles from town. The backdrop was dominated by sage-covered buttes cut by a long, wide-open valley bisected by the transcontinental railroad mainline. It was a sparse land ruled by alkali tides and the stinginess of Mother Nature. The only vegetation, tufts of crested wheat grass and wild oats, refused to yield to drought, grazing animals or the insults of man. Every sunset looked like it came from a paint-by-number kit. Quail punctuated the setting sun by throwing back their heads and breaking the oppressive silence with their well-rehearsed trill; *"One last cheer! One last cheer! One last cheer!"*

Cowboys moved cattle across the range. Miners dug in the dry, rocky soil. Railroaders pushed freight and passengers east and west. Bored salesmen and travelers passed, coming and going on Highway 51. When *Red's Place* finally did open, any of these men wanting to pay-to-play pulled off the road and walked into an opulent palace devoted to just one thing, their pleasure.

Red demanded that her ladies act with proper etiquette and guests conduct themselves as gentlemen. Bad language or vulgarities were strictly forbidden. Men wanting to purchase pleasure were expected to make innocent requests, such as: "I'd like to talk to Bobbi," or "Could I buy Monica a drink?" or "If Jeree is available I'd like to say hello."

If a customer was unfamiliar with the ladies, or if a regular wanted to have a look at any recent additions to the line, Red rang her silver bell. The available ladies emerged from behind a red curtain and Red made the necessary introductions. A man might engage several of the ladies in conversation, perhaps buy a round of drinks, but when he had made his selection he spoke to Red and they discretely talked price for the services requested. She had one hard-and-fast rule; all money was collected before services were rendered.

The ladies employed were more than workers with willing attitudes and moneymaking bodies. Each lady became a member of Red's family. They were the daughters she had never been able to have, and over the years she watched many of her lovely daughters blossom into wives and mothers, or to continue their formal education and have fulfilling professional careers.

As in any family, there were occasional conflicts and rivalries. At *Red's Place* these were magnified each time a man came to the door because several ladies were waiting to compete for his attention, and his money. The ladies established a pecking order based upon their popularity and earning capacity. Often an older lady, who was not as favored as the younger ones, deceitfully tried to advise the more desirable lady to "Change your hair," or "Don't wear that," or "Don't waste your time with him, he's a cheapskate," or "Stay away from him, he's a problem just waiting to happen."

Red concluded most ladies involved in the profession of prostitution wanted one of two things; momentary power over a man, or his money. There were exceptions to every rule. One was CeCe, an exotic beauty of French and Chinese parentage. She said she was willing to work until she had saved enough to purchase a Harley Davidson motorcycle. True to her word, the day she bought the cherry red Sportster, she gave her notice and roared off into the sunset.

Red spent time becoming educated in the multitude of ways men seek satisfaction. The challenge for her was to talk to each man and discover his most intimate fantasy, and for a certain price, she was willing to make that fantasy come true. But not every man who stepped through the door of *Red's Place* wanted gratification in a traditional fashion, or through some wild fantasy. Some were merely lonely men who wanted nothing more vigorous than an intellectual conversation. Others were physically incapable of performing and simply wished to share the company of a female in a romantic setting. Some paid to observe others entangled in the act of sex.

▯▯▯▯▯▯▯

Red ran her business, and on the side kept her arrangement with Mike, making infrequent trips to see him in San Francisco. On one of these visits, they were seated in a restaurant with a panoramic view of the Golden Gate Bridge. Lights glittered off the water like tiny stars. Red reflected on how, when she was a kid, she used to think stars were the lights of people who had died. Her mother was the morning star and her father the evening star.

"Are you happy?"

"How the hell would I know something like that off the top of my head?"

The waiter appeared and asked if they might be interested in taking a look at the dessert tray. Mike said, "Just coffee. Two. Black." He waited until the coffee was served and then took a quick sip and fidgeted.

"There's a little matter we need to discuss."

Red had endured a 500-mile train ride from Elko, a lengthy dinner and now all she wanted was a good night's sleep. "What is it?"

"This isn't easy."

"Don't drag it out. Just tell me."

"Last time I was home you were too busy to see me—I'm not using that as an excuse or anything—but something happened."

"For Christ's sake, Mike, what happened?"

"I guess I got lonely. I met this girl, thought we'd have a few laughs. Just so you know she was the one who came on to me."

"A one-time matinee, or did you follow it up?" Red told herself she really didn't care.

"We got together a few times, okay. I shipped out. She went her way. I went mine. When I got back there was a letter waiting for me." He paused to gather himself like a horse will do before leaping an irrigation ditch. A waitress walked past and he diverted his attention to watch the way the tiny tendons behind her knees flexed against her nylons with each stride.

"To make a long story short, she went and got herself pregnant."

"She didn't go and *get herself pregnant*. How do you know you're the father?"

"She said I was."

"And you believe her?"

"No reason not to. Yeah."

"Who is this girl?"

"You want her name?"

"Yes. What's her name."

"Jaylynne MacGruder."

"McGown and MacGruder. M and M. Sounds like candy. How nice. How old is she?"

"Twenty-one."

"Asshole! What were you thinking?"

"I'm sorry."

"Don't apologize. That only makes it worse." She lit a cigarette off the butt of the last one and took a drag. "I'll make a telephone call and have this mess taken care of."

"Too late."

"When's she due?"

"June. Middle of June."

"Is she planning on keeping it, or giving it up for adoption?"

"Giving it up."

At one time Red had wanted to be a mother more than anything, but that dream had withered and died long ago. She might not be capable of conceiving, but her husband sure as hell could father a child.

"I want the baby. I'll raise it."

"You can't...."

"I'll handle this. You arrange for me to meet this girl then you stay the hell out of it. If I find you're meddling behind my back, I'll take a gun and shoot it off." She nodded in the general direction of his groin.

┆┆┆┆┆┆┆

When Red met Jaylynne, she was surprised by the young lady's fears; scared how the physical and financial implications of giving birth might affect her. Jaylynne viewed her pregnancy as a terrible disruption to her freedom, and to her ability to just have fun.

Red seized upon those fears as an opportunity and used them to control the young woman. Red proposed she would assume all financial obligations, including moving Jaylynne into an apartment until the baby was born, and then taking the baby and raising it in a stable and loving home. Her stipulations were that Jaylynne must agree to sign away her rights, and once the child was born, to have no further involvement. If these two conditions were agreed upon, Jaylynne would receive a $1,000 cash settlement. The papers were drawn up and Jaylynne willingly signed.

The baby, a girl, was born and Red named her Cindy Marie. Through a financial arrangement with an unprincipled doctor, Red was listed as the birth mother. Mike, of course, was recorded as the father.

The first time Red held Cindy Marie in her arms—such tiny fingers and toes, fine curly hair as black as Mike's had once been, nose straight, lovely mouth—she was filled with wonder and contentment. She kissed the baby's forehead and could feel warmth and vitality pulsing below the skin. She watched the heart beating strongly through the soft spot on the top of Cindy Marie's well-rounded head. Brown eyes, anxious and inquisitive, opened wide.

One of the nurses brought a bottle of formula and showed Red how to sprinkle a few drops on her wrist to make sure the formula was not too hot or too cold. She held the nipple to Cindy Marie's mouth. As she began to suckle, Red felt the immense weight of her lifetime of frustration and loneliness being lifted and replaced with the joys of motherhood. At long last she had someone who needed her, someone she could give her total love to, and someone who would return that love. A wave of gratitude swept over her. Tears came naturally. "Thank you. Thank you, Lord."

Jaylynne never had the opportunity to hold the precious child she pushed into this world. She went through the birthing process, spent three days in the hospital recuperating, and upon checking out was handed a sealed envelope containing ten crisp one hundred dollar bills.

It was months later that Red received a telephone call.

"I have a collect call from Jaylynne MacGruder. Will you accept the charges?"

Red ground her cigarette into the ashtray as though it was a vivid exclamation point at the end of a long, rambling sentence. "Yes, I will."

"You may go ahead," the operator said.

"Hello."

Even though it was a single word, Red knew Jaylynne had been drinking and was emotionally distraught. She did not want to be a part of this young woman's troubles.

"Our agreement was you were to never contact me."

Jaylynne cried, sniffled and whimpered. "I need help."

"Pull it together. What do you need?"

Jaylynne blubbered something convoluted about being in Las Vegas, owing someone money, and an unpaid hotel bill. She blew her nose and then Red heard ice cubes clink against glass. When Jaylynne came back on the line, her words and their intent were unclouded.

"If you don't help me I'm going to court and take back my baby."

Red asked the name of the hotel where Jaylynne was staying and her room number. The words she spoke next were as cold as icicles clinging to eaves. "Stay where you are. I'll be there and take care of this."

Red knew she should hang up the phone, but she did not, not right away. She placed her hand over the mouthpiece and stayed on the line, listening to the empty hiss of all the intervening miles and Jaylynne's ragged breathing. The silence could not be read any more than blank pages in a book. When she came to that realization, she replaced the receiver on the cradle so deliberately she was not quite sure the exact instant the line went dead.

Red, after making arrangements for one of her girls to care for Cindy Marie, drove south on Highway 51, toward Jiggs and Eureka. Six hours and 19 minutes after hanging up the phone, and having crossed the expansive state of Nevada from north to south, she arrived in Las Vegas. She pulled up in front of the hotel, gave her keys to the valet, located Jaylynne's room and rapped her knuckles on the door. Nothing happened. She knocked again. The door finally opened and there was Jaylynne looking disheveled, sleepy-eyed and hung over. Red pushed past her into the room.

"Don't you ever try and blackmail me again. Legally that baby is mine. I want you to understand this. I hired a private detective to find your mother and father. I know who they are and where they live. Get this straight—and this isn't some idle threat—if you do not disappear from my life, and stay that way, I will get in touch with your mother and father. I will tell them you slept with a married man, tried to have an abortion, gave up your baby and are blackmailing me. The choice is yours. What are you going to do?"

Jaylynne sank onto the bed and burst into tears. Feeling a sudden pang of sympathy for this young woman, Red got a towel from the bathroom. She tossed the towel across Jaylynne's knees. She picked it up and dabbed at her eyes with the towel.

"I owe $900. He said he'd cut off my hands if I don't get him the money. I can't pay. I'm afraid. I didn't know what to do. Please, this one time, can you help me? Please."

Red opened her purse, counted out nine hundred-dollar bills and forcefully tossed them onto the bed, along with some advice. "Go home. Find yourself a nice man. Get married. Have a dozen kids.

"I'll pay your hotel bill this one time. But don't you dare, as long as you live, ever pull a stunt like this again."

Chapter Nineteen

When he was on the outs with Kay, Jack became a drifter, traveling between one of his many mining claims scattered around the remote recesses of the Western states or working as a journalist for a string of small town weekly newspapers. If not engaged in one of those activities, he spent time pecking away at the typewriter keys in an ambitious attempt to write a novel. His manuscript, which had grown to more than 400 pages, was drawn from events in his own life. Jack titled his manuscript, *Out to Set the World on Fire*.

On the night he and Kelsey ran away from home that was exactly what they thought they were going to do, set the world on fire. Jack's big dream was that his manuscript would be published by a New York house. In return, he was hoping to receive literary acclaim and a measure of financial security.

┼┼┼┼┼┼

Jack sat in front of his green and white manual Smith-Corona portable typewriter. His stubby fingers struck at keys, trying to keep up with his thoughts, trying to make sense of the dreadful news he felt compelled to share with Nellie.

273

Even though he had seen his sister only a few times in the last decade or so, she remained his constant, the one person he could always count on.

Dearest Nel,

This hurts to put into words, but I feel you should know. Not long ago Kay got hold of me and asked me to come home. It turned out she has cancer. It's as bad as it can get.

I know this is a shock to you. It certainly was to me. I've been living with her these past few months, caring for her. She must have been sick for a good long while but she never let on, anyway not to me. The doctors wanted to operate and put her on an aggressive course of chemotherapy and radiation. She refused treatment, saying she would rather die on her own terms. I admire her for that.

Yesterday I checked her into the care facility in Salem. She has her own room and they have her on a morphine drip. The doctor says it's only a matter of time. I'll write again.

With Love,

Jack

He finished the letter in the gray light of early morning, deliberately unrolled the white paper from the typewriter carriage, folded it neatly and slipped it into an envelope that he would mail. He shrugged on his coat and put on his hat. He took the box containing his unfinished manuscript and went to the Hospice center. As he walked down a long hallway, the air he breathed was stuffy and smelled of Lysol. He passed open doors and caught quick glances at patients propped up in beds.

He knew these people, their bodies ravished by disease or old age and beyond repair, were fighting desperately, unreasonably, to hang on to a few more moments of life.

He entered Kay's room, pulled a chair near her bed. She was unconscious. He sat and watched her breathing; shallow and ragged. He removed his manuscript from the box and began reading. He read until his voice was nearly gone, and still he continued to read. When he finished the last page he returned the manuscript to the box, stood and spoke in a soft whisper, telling Kay he loved her, had always loved her, and would always love her. He leaned close and planted a tender kiss on her forehead. His lips touched skin that was blue, cold and clammy. She had slipped away while he read to her.

▚▚▚▚▚▚

At Kay's funeral, Jack wanted to say something of substance, something insightful that would define her life. He wanted to speak from his heart and reveal why, through all the intervening years and despite their chaotic relationship, he had remained steadfastly in love with her. But her passing was too excruciatingly painful and he was too emotionally sensitive. He listened to others speak, but he remained silent.

After the graveside service, he was approached by one of Kay's friends who inquired what he was going to do now that she was gone. He said he did not know, and then like a soldier defeated in battle, he hung his head, limped away, got in his pickup truck and began to drive. He had no destination in mind, did not really care where he went, or when he got there. His only thought was to put distance between himself and her body, lying in a pioneer cemetery on top of the Waldo Hills overlooking the green bosom of the Willamette Valley.

He drove south and east, camping one night on the desert near Burns. The country he passed through was a sandy wasteland populated with sagebrush and an occasional tortured juniper tree. Ahead on the road he saw something; a solitary magpie working on a road kill. The long-tailed bird took one last impertinent peck, and with a thrusting of wings lifted into flight, chopping the air into flashes of black and white. The brittle late afternoon sunlight intensified the similarity of the bird's plumage and the fur of a recently killed skunk on the road. Jack hurriedly cranked his window handle, but was not fast enough, and as spinning wheels straddled the ripe polecat the putrid smell swept into the cab causing his eyes to immediately water and his stomach to convulse. He pinched his nostrils closed, steered with a knee, rolled down the window and finally, when he absolutely had to draw a breath, he leaned out the window as far as he could and took fresh air into his lungs. He was several miles down the road before the offensive smell began to dissipate inside the cab.

Upon reaching Carlin, Nevada, he stopped at a Union 76 station and filled the pickup's tank with gas. He washed the windshield and went inside where he bought a loaf of bread, some luncheon meat and a beer. He fixed a bologna sandwich and washed it down with the beer.

After leaving town, heading south on Highway 51, he crossed a bridge over the thin and languid Humboldt River. Ahead was a railroad crossing, its red lights flashing, white arm swinging down to block the highway. He pulled his foot off the gas, tapped the brake a time or two and the pickup began to slow. He coasted to a stop. A long moment passed, and then a westbound diesel locomotive came thundering down the track pushing before it a violent wave that shook the ground and caused the air to shudder. The hard charging locomotive was dragging a long line of freight cars; some painted with colorful graffiti and others a drab rusty red or faded yellow. Images blurred.

Jack recalled having passed this way another time, years before. He and Kelsey had been riding in a coal gondola. Palisade Canyon, the scene of his accident, was just a short distance away, off down the tracks. He looked to his right, toward the receding train and could see the outline of the canyon's yawning mouth. He was struck with an irrational fear, a fear that his weathered and misshapen boot, with bones inside, was still out there lying beside the track.

The train passed and the white arm swung to a vertical position. Jack drew a ragged breath and shoved the transmission into gear. He let out the clutch, and the pickup bumped up and over the set of tracks. After traveling a few miles, he saw a welcoming sign advertising *Red's Place*. He told himself he needed a drink to calm his frayed nerves and steered onto the graveled parking area.

Stepping through the doorway and into the dimly lit interior, Jack waited for his eyes to adjust a little before shuffling across the hardwood floor and climbing onto a stool. A woman stood behind the bar. She had striking red hair and was about the same age as Jack. She greeted him with, "What's your pleasure, mister?"

"Beer."

"Any particular flavor?"

"Whatever you got, long as it's cold."

The woman pulled a brown bottle from a galvanized tub where it lay on a bed of ice and opened it with a practiced flick of her wrist. She set the beer on the bar in front of Jack. Beads of condensation busily formed and ran down the brown glass like sad tears. He picked up the bottle and took a long swig.

"Interested in seeing the line?"

Jack set the bottle on the bar. His brow furrowed as he processed what the woman had said; then glancing around, he broke into laughter.

"You know, my first impression was this was a pretty dang fancy outfit for a country bar. Now I know. Sometimes it takes me longer than others, but eventually I do catch on. I'll just have my beer and be on my way. But thanks."

"Well, if you change your mind...."

He chuckled softly, and in the empty room it sounded like footfalls creaking on snow. "I'm too damn old for monkey business."

The woman gave him a teasing wink. "You got that wrong, mister. You're never too old for a little monkey business." She extended her hand. "I'm Red. I own this place."

Jack shook her hand and introduced himself. Since it was a Sunday evening, and there were no customers, the two strangers began to visit. Their conversation flowed easily. Jack spoke about Kay, her battle with cancer and the funeral.

"We never did get married. All the same I loved her the best I could. Guess it was just never enough." He sipped his beer.

It was highly unusually for Red to talk about herself, and yet she found herself telling him about her hilltop home with a panoramic view of Elko, the Humboldt River Valley and beyond to the snowcapped Ruby Mountains.

"I love to stand in front of the window and watch the ever-changing moods where mountains meet sky. In the spring of the year the valley blushes green, in summer the hills bake in the sun and turn a pale tan, and in autumn the aspen leaves define the mountainside draws in shimmering shades of yellow and gold. The coming of winter dusts the summits and each day the white blanket is tugged lower and lower, until snow finally coats the valley floor."

Jack sipped his beer and Red drank iced tea doctored with an artificial sweetener. Before she knew what she was doing, Red was telling him the particulars of her marriage to Mike, his ascension up the maritime ladder to become captain of an

American Transport Service tug hauling cargo barges to the farthest reaches of the Pacific Ocean. She mentioned that a couple of times a year he still called and she met him in San Francisco or he traveled to Elko. She even told about her daughter, Cindy Marie.

"Of course I had to have a nanny, but the first word my little girl ever spoke, she spoke to me. It was 'Momma.' I was there when she took her first step. I was Santa Claus, the Easter Bunny and the Tooth Fairy all rolled into one. Sometimes, I would just stare at her. No child has ever been loved as much as my Cindy Marie. She filled up my life, made it complete and flawless.

"When she got a little older it scared me. I though she might want to know where her momma disappeared to each afternoon and evening, and when she asked me that question I told her a little white lie. I said I owned a ranch and had to check and make sure the cowboys were taking care of the cows.

"One day, Cindy Marie asked, 'May I have a horse, Momma?'

"I told her we didn't have room for a horse.

"And her response was, 'But, Momma, couldn't we keep him at the ranch?'

"What could I do? I bought a ranch, a 3,000-acre cattle ranch in Starr Valley, a half-hour's drive east from Elko. I installed a ranch manager to grow hay, care for the cattle and watch over the little black pony with four matching stockings and the white star on its forehead that Santa brought to Cindy Marie. Nearly every Sunday morning, we made the drive to Starr Valley so she could visit the pony she named Midnight and ride in circles around the pole corral."

Cindy Marie attended first, second and third grades at the public elementary school in Elko. All the while, Red was uneasy knowing that at any moment, on the playground or walking home after school, some classmate could spill the beans and describe in graphic detail the scandalous truth, that her mother was the notorious whorehouse madam of *Red's Place*.

Her uneasiness became an irrational fear. If Cindy Marie discovered her mother lied once, in later years she might keep digging until she uncovered the fact her mother could not possibly be her mother. What then?

Red had sent Cindy Marie away to Catholic boarding school in Reno. She came home once a month and spent summer vacations at the ranch, living with the manager's family. If she ever was made aware of her mother's secret, she never let on.

"I've been rambling like a school girl on her first date. Let me buy you a beer, Jack, and you can tell me how you happened to come west. Where did you say you were from? Nebraska wasn't it?"

╞╪╪╪╪╪╡

Jack told about running away from home, hoboing his way west, and was describing the series of events leading up to his accident west of Elko. Red suddenly placed both hands on the table and leaned closer. Her eyes widened with interest.

"When was this?"

"Middle of May, 19 and 28."

"Was it storming that night? Lightning and thundering? Was there sleet and snow?"

"Yeah. One hell of a bad storm came up. It was damned cold for that time of year."

Jack went on to tell about the accident in which he lost his leg.

"Afterward, did the train stop?"

"Yup. My traveling partner stopped it."

"Did he run the spine? Is he the one that got the engineer to stop the train?"

Jack's brow was knit. He looked confused.

"The train pulled onto a siding. After a while an eastbound train came alongside. You were transferred to that train. They probably took you back to the doctor in Elko. That must have been you."

"How do you know all that?"

"Because...I was riding that train."

That night, Red allowed Jack to sleep in one of the unused rooms. The following day he mentioned he was attempting to write a book and promised that someday he would allow Red to read it. But he said he needed a couple of months to be alone and put the finishing touches on the manuscript. He asked if Red knew of a place he could rent, nothing fancy he said, just a roof over his head.

"Know just the spot. Part of my summer range is on a BLM allotment north of town. There's a line shack up there. It's not much to look at, but it's livable. No electricity. No telephone. It's perched on a ridge overlooking the North Fork of the Humboldt River and has a wonderful view. You can see the Ruby Mountains from up there and as far north as Hat Peak on the Duck Valley Indian Reservation. Real pretty. Why don't you go there? Stay as long as you want."

"How much?"

"Nothing, You'd be doing me a favor. If you're there, things won't grow legs and walk away."

Red drew a map, and after Jack loaded up on groceries, he drove the rutted dirt road to the line shack. He swept the rough wood floor so enthusiastically that dust danced in the bars of light slanting through the sunny windows. He put his staples away in the cupboard, threw his sleeping bag on the bunk and turned his full attention to working on his manuscript. He banged out letters and words, sentences and paragraphs on the green and white manual typewriter he had dragged around with him for better than three decades.

When he was not working, he read books and magazines, went for walks and used the windowsill as a rest to shoot tin cans off a rock with a single-shot .22. He did not have a television, radio or a newspaper and had absolutely no desire to know the happenings of the day.

Jack liked the look of the rustic cabin hanging out there on the exposed backbone of Calimus Ridge. He inspected the exterior for any signs of peeling, chipping or flaking, and found none. There was no sign the place had ever seen a coat of paint. He liked that too and told himself every house should be left to the devices of the cold north wind and the hard bake of the summer sun. Paint was something a woman insisted on. As if paint, especially white paint, whiter than bleached bones, could coat and cover up whatever problems happened to exist. Up here on top of the world those problems were isolation, solitude, loneliness. He could tell no woman had ever stayed more than a night or two in this line shack. And that too was fine with him.

If Kay was alive she might have asked, "What are you doing, trying to be a hermit?"

He probably would have answered, "You know me. I never have fit in. I'm just living here and doing exactly what I want to do, putting words on paper. I'm happy. Who knows? Maybe when I get done, I'll have me a best seller."

It was in late October when Jack reappeared at *Red's Place* with a cardboard box tied shut with a leather bootlace. He took a seat and laid the box in front of him on the bar. He told Red, "Here you go. Read it. Tell me what you think."

"You finished your book? Congratulations. Let me buy you a beer."

But Jack was already up and strolling across the room. When he reached the door, he tossed over his shoulder, "Just read," and he was gone.

Red untied the bootlace, opened the box and began reading the manuscript. She read through the afternoon and into evening.

⊢⊢⊢⊢⊢⊢⊣

Jack returned to the line shack as the colors of the day were draining toward darkness. He took the coal oil lamp from the shelf, set it on the table and lit the wick with a stick match he struck on the underside of the table. For a time he sat in a straight-backed chair and watched the flame flutter— sometimes yellow, sometimes orange, occasionally blue. He was wearing faded red long johns that showed through the worn elbows of his plaid shirt. The veins on the back of his hands were visible as pale blue lines and his skin was as paper-thin as a hornet's nest. He returned his portable typewriter to its case, zipped it shut, and placed the case on the table beside the wooden box containing the letters he had written his mother so many years before. His fingertips absently traced along the contours of the box. Then he turned down the wick on the lamp and sat in the murky light undecided as to what he should do next. He rose and went outside, closing the door securely behind him. A stifling quiet rushed in and surrounded him. The quiet was all-powerful, almost godlike.

As he began to move, pain shot up his bad leg like a plowshare breaking through hard sod. After several halting steps, the pain mostly went away and the function of movement became easier. He walked in a silent world where stars filled the darkness, stars as busy as fireflies. The Milky Way radiated high overhead in a luminous arc. Behind him, the lamp, as seen through the window of the line shack, became as distant as just one more twinkling star and then it winked out. There was the great diamond of Orion the Hunter, rising up phosphorescent against the sheet of inky blackness. In the opposite corner of the sky the Big Dipper spun around the North Star, measuring the curve of time, one night passing slowly.

Muffled sounds became audible: an owl raked the air as it coasted in front of the stars, the thin rattle of a cricket's wings, a cold-blooded bull snake rustling dry skin as it slid deeper into the warm pocket in the crevice between rocks. A light wind now sighed softly, blowing through the canyons below.

Off to the west, a flow of cool, moist Pacific air crashed against the desert heat and lightning glowed mutely in the distance like a welder's torch busily repairing some small flawed spot on the far side of the world. A blue spark pulsed. A long moment later a thin splinter of thunder reached Jack, a sound no louder than if he had stepped on a dry twig.

There was more lightning and thunder, moving steadily nearer and nearer until at last a brilliant flash overhead turned the night to day for a quivering instant. Thunder cracked, echoing and re-echoing, rolling across the broad landscape the way a shot from a high-powered rifle will do. Blackness prevailed. Rain poured down. Jack recalled it had been a night similar to this when...lightning, rain, the train, Palisade....

The storm passed quickly. Now, far off to the east, tiny flashes of blue-white light continued to throb. The rattle of thunder was once again distant and subdued. His pants, wet from the rain, clung close to his bony hips. If he had been able to see into the night, he might have caught sight of a herd of antelope moving along through the sage at an easy canter; and been able to recognize their wanderings were as aimless as his life.

The morning star flared, signaling the start of a malignant dawn. Feeble light transformed the night. The desert terrain turned a neutral gray as far as the eye could see. A jackrabbit rose from its haunches and slinked through the sage. Turkey vultures left their perch in a snag and laboriously flapped their wings in an attempt to find a rising thermal. A dead foal lay stretched in the tainted grasses, eyeless, with hide pulled taut over a withered summit of rib bones. Far below, a languid stream like a long black snake, slithered aimlessly where the meadow stretched between the confines of the hills. A noisy flock of red-winged blackbirds rose in unison from the meadow and were followed in tight pursuit by a goshawk. The blackbirds settled in the safety of the willows and chastised the hawk as it flashed away, circling, patiently waiting for the deadly chase to resume.

Rainwater in the cupped hands of a rock reflected the cool layer of silver that was now being traced along the eastern horizon. Jack paused, got down on hands and shaky knees and awkwardly bent forward. His quivering lips broke the thin veneer as he drank the liquid from the natural bowl. After satisfying his thirst, he sat and watched as a flutter of red surged into a narrow band of sky like blood seeping through water. The intensity drained away and the sky softened. A thin crescent of ripe yellow broke over the brow of a hill as round as the curve of a woman's hip. With the rising sun, the bleak scene, scrubbed fresh from the rain, began the process of transforming itself into a rainbow of lively colors.

He slumped bleary-eyed and weary against the solidness of the rock. Maybe he slept because when his eyes came open for the last time the sun was floating in a sky pleated with unsympathetic clouds welded to the tall, blue sky—time hung suspended—and then the clouds came tumbling down.

╫╫╫╫╫╫

A pair of mounted buckaroos—toothpicks in their hatbands and the sour smell of strong coffee on their breath—followed a cow trail. One of them tugged on the reins, removed his hat, allowed the morning breeze to cool his forehead, and then replaced the hat. He dug around in his shirt pocket, pulled loose a snuff can, tapped the lid a time or two, pried it open and used two fingers and a thumb to take a dip. He pushed a gob of brown tobacco into place under his lower lip and positioned it just so with his tongue. He spit stray flakes onto the ground, replaced the lid, again tapped the can as was his habit to do, and returned it to his shirt pocket. While he was so occupied his horse tipped a hind foot and started to sleep. A red-tailed hawk skated diagonally across the sky. The buckaroo became aware of human footprints in the soft, sandy soil.

"Some gol dang fool's out here afoot," he drawled to his , partner. "Been since the storm. Best have a look-see."

The second man said nothing. The first rolled his tongue against his molars making a clicking sound that woke up his horse and the horse moved in the direction the tracks were leading. Less than a mile down the trail the buckaroos came upon a body leaned against a boulder. From the look of contentment on the man's face, it was as if he sat down and simply fell asleep.

THE END

Rick Steber, the author of more than forty books and sales of more than a million copies, has received national acclaim for his writing. His numerous awards include the Western Writers of America Spur Award for Best Western Novel, Independent Publishers Award—Best Regional Fiction, Western Heritage Award, Benjamin Franklin Award, Mid-America Publishers Award, Oregon Library Association Award and Oregon Literary Arts Award. Two of his books have been optioned to movie production companies.

In addition to his writing, Rick is an engaging Western personality and has the unique ability to make his characters come alive as he tells a story. He has spoken at national and international conferences and visits schools where he talks to students about the importance of education, developing reading and writing skills, and impressing upon them the value of saving our history for future generations.

Rick has two sons, Seneca and Dusty. He lives near Prineville, Oregon and writes in a cabin in the timbered foothills of the Ochoco Mountains.

Acknowledgement

With special thanks to the following individuals: Mark Christensen, Alys Means, Terry Romero, Suzie Downing, Katherine Yoakum Nitsch, Kathleen Howard, Pamela Laughton Glave, Kristine Taylor, Laura McShane, Valarie Motanic and Jody Conners.